abc's of
HAM RADIO

by HOWARD S. PYLE, W7OE

 HOWARD W. SAMS & CO., INC.
THE BOBBS-MERRILL CO., INC.
INDIANAPOLIS · KANSAS CITY · NEW YORK

THIRD EDITION

FOURTH PRINTING—1972

International Standard Book Number: 0-672-20638-2
Library of Congress Catalog Card Number: 68-21361

Preface

This book is devoted to introducing you to the fascinating hobby of ham radio. I have been a radio amateur for more than half a century and have taught classes in both novice and advanced amateur radio for many years. The material in this book is essentially the same as that presented in my classrooms. I have made every attempt to present the necessary information for obtaining an amateur radio novice license in as entertaining as well as instructive manner as possible. It has been most gratifying to find that the first two editions of this book have served admirably to prepare students for the Federal license examination. This updated and expanded third edition should be even more helpful. All the changes introduced by the new incentive licensing program have been incorporated in this edition.

ABC's of Ham Radio offers you all of the data essential to understanding the basic principles of electricity and its radio applications, together with the applicable radio laws and regulations. You will not be confused by a maze of wiring diagrams, radio and electrical symbols, schematics, formulas, equations, and similar extraneous material—none of this is required to become an apprentice to the amateur radio ranks. There is time enough for concentrated study of more intricate information leading to the higher grades of amateur radio licenses *after* you have acquired your novice "ticket."

Welcome to the serious, but light, study of the following pages which, together with an elementary knowledge of the radiotelegraph code, will lead to the issuance of your novice-class license and to the many, many pleasurable hours you will derive from one of the finest hobbies in the world. Good luck!

HOWARD S. PYLE

In 1964 the youngest licensed U.S. radio amateur was Gary Lewis, WN7BBJ. Gary received his novice license at the tender age of seven. Since that time he has received his general/conditional license.

Ham radio is by no means limited to the male element. Pictured above is Gary's mother, Mary, W7QGP with the impressive station equipment she has owned and operated for several years.

At the opposite end of the age group, Herb Coffin, WB6TTV of San Diego, California. Herb passed his novice examination and received his license in May 1965 at the age of 75.

Contents

1

About the Exam

1-1. *ABC's of Ham Radio* has been prepared for the sole purpose of introducing you to the fascinating international hobby of amateur radio. In the following chapters we take you through a study of the requirements for securing a novice radio amateur's license. These requirements consist of some knowledge of the radiotelegraph code and a written examination comprising some twenty questions of which you must answer at least three-fourths correctly to secure a passing grade. That these questions are elementary is borne out by the fact that children as young as seven and eight years old have successfully passed the examination and secured their novice licenses! Octogenarians as well as those of all intermediate ages have done likewise.

1-2. No knowledge of wiring diagrams or symbols is required. You need have no more than the most elemental idea of basic electricity and radio, and this we give you in the pages to follow. You need know nothing about radio receivers. The Federal Communications Commission (FCC) is concerned only that you have sufficient knowledge of radio *transmitters* to insure that you can operate them legally. The same applies to Radio Laws and Regulations. Just as you are expected, in taking an examination for an automobile driver's license, to be familiar with certain rules governing motor vehicle operation, so you must know the regulations applying to amateur radio operation.

1-3. The average time for the written examination is forty-five minutes. Like any subject, the more familiar you are with it, the more quickly can you answer the questions. Those for the radio amateur novice examination are of the multiple-choice type; that is, you will receive a printed sheet containing the questions with five possible answers to each. You are only required to choose the answer you believe to be correct and to so indicate on the answer sheet by marking the appropriate letter—*a, b, c, d,* or *e*—in the space provided.

1-4. You need not appear at a federal office for your novice examination. Only the general, advanced, and extra classes of amateur examinations require appearance before an engineer of the Federal Communications Commission. For the novice and technician grades, the examination can be taken in your own home, that of your examiner, or at some other place and at such time as suits your (and his) convenience. Your examiner (selected by you) must be either an amateur who holds a valid general, advanced, or extra class radio operator license, a commercial radio*telegraph* license, or a United States Government radiotelegraph operator. The examiner may be of either sex, but must be at least 21 years of age.

1-5. Many of the examination questions are of the "memory answer" type; you need only study the question and memorize the correct answer. This is particularly true with respect to the Laws and Regulations. For example, you would memorize the fact that the maximum penalty for violation of any of the rules and regulations of the Federal Communications Commission is "$500.00 *per day* for each day the offense occurs, plus the suspension of the *operator* license and revocation of the *station* license." This, of course, will be the only correct answer.

1-6. Some examination answers will be obvious; ordinary intelligence and common sense will dictate which one is proper. The sample questions appearing on the following pages are not the actual ones which will appear on your formal examination sheet. However, they are of the same multiple-choice type; the wording and intent will be similar. For example, perhaps you will be asked, "Which of the following instruments is used to measure power? (*a*) ohmmeter; (*b*) wattmeter; (*c*) ammeter; (*d*) voltmeter; (*e*) wavemeter." The same may appear as a statement rather than as a question: "Electrical power is measured by: (*a*) voltmeter; (*b*) ammeter (*c*) ohmmeter; (*d*) wattmeter; (*e*) wavemeter." The correct answer to either form, or one of similar wording, will be the same.

1-7. All of the preceding material and that on the following pages is authentic and has been carefully checked with authoritative sources to ensure its accuracy. You may rely upon its constituting the minimum requirements for preparing yourself for the novice examination. We have, however, allowed a ten percent "safety factor" by carrying explanatory matter slightly beyond that which you will actually need to know. This will be of considerable assistance to you in interpreting the examination questions.

1-8. For those readers who desire to qualify for their novice class license in a minimum of time, a guided course of study with a recognized training school, will prove most satisfactory. Until recently no such course was offered by any of the nationally recognized electronics training institutions. However, the National Radio Institute, 3939 Wisconsin Ave., Washington, D. C. 20016, has now introduced such a course designed exclusively to prepare students for the amateur radio novice license examination. To the best of our knowledge, this is the first and currently the only institution to make such training available through a homestudy correspondence course.

1-9. There you have it. You want to engage in this glorious hobby as soon as possible and with the least effort. You want to do it legally, so your first approach is through the novice or apprentice ranks. That is the purpose of this book—to make your indoctrination into ham radio easy, quick, and painless!

2

The Radiotelegraph Code

2-1. Before discussing the written section of the examination, suppose we consider the requirements for the *code* portion. Many aspiring amateurs are puzzled by the necessity for learning the radio code. They ask, "Why do we have to learn the code when we intend to operate by voice only?" There are many reasons why. Military, naval, and commercial interests have found that communication by dot and dash is far more accurate than the spoken word. In the code (which in radio parlance is referred to as *CW*, meaning *continuous-wave telegraphy*), each letter is represented by a combination of *dots* and *dashes*. At first thought, this may appear to the layman to be a laborious method. Actually, it is not. Competent operators, completely familiar with the code, can snap it out at approximately thirty-five to forty-five words per minute. In normal, experienced amateur communication practice, the speed is somewhat less, around twenty-five words per minute. However, by the intelligent use of abbreviations, this speed can be almost doubled. For example, in a modified form of the Phillips code (a system of standardized abbreviations which you need not learn for the examination), the word *the* is sent simply as the letter *t*; the word *that* as *tt*, *have* as *hv*, etc. The result through use of Phillips and at a sending speed of 25 words per minute is to convey intelligence at an approximate rate of *fifty* words per minute. The abbreviations of the Phillips code are *not* used in actual transmission of formal messages, however; each word is carefully spelled out just as the sender wrote it. Where faster transmission or reception is required, as in busy commercial stations, *automatic* transmission is used. In this system, characters are punched into a paper tape (Fig. 2-1) by means of a keyboard similar to that of a typewriter. This tape, in turn, is run at high speeds (200-300 words a minute) through mechanisms which *key* the radio transmitter—in other words, break up the radio emissions into the dots and dashes comprising the International radiotelegraph code. This

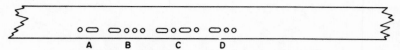

Fig. 2-1. Perforated paper tape used in automatic code transmission.

is the type of tape transmission used by such amateur code-practice stations as W1AW of the American Radio Relay League and their volunteer member stations. Here the tape is sent at 5 to 35 words per minute to give beginning operators a chance to practice their code.

2-2. Such high-speed transmission is received on a paper tape, on which the characters appear as a printed line in a square formation (Fig. 2-2). An operator who is skilled in reading this line by sight, interprets the letters and figures, and reproduces them on a typewriter. The automatic transmission, at 300 words per minute, can be divided among ten "sight" operators by cutting the received tape. It is obvious that, even though each operator will be reading the tape at only thirty words per minute, the final result is reception at 300 words per minute!

2-3. Sound a bit confusing? Then study Fig. 2-2, which is an example of the printed characters received by an automatic tape receiver (called a siphon recorder). This is the way the message appears to the sight operator. He merely interprets the "radio

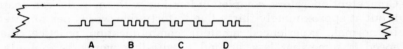

Fig. 2-2. The code characters of Fig. 2-1, as reproduced on paper tape by a siphon recorder.

shorthand," as a stenographer does the curlicues she produces from her boss's dictation. Amateur reception is almost exclusively by ear. The cost of siphon recorders, as well as the time element in learning to read by sight, limits their usage by amateurs. The amateur station equipped with such intricate devices is indeed a rarity.

2-4. Now let's consider a bit more the accuracy of CW over phone transmission. The phonetics of speech are highly variable. For instance, the male voice is ordinarily much deeper than the lilting trill of the female. Common to both sexes is a wide variation in the frequencies of their spoken words. A good, legal radiophone transmitter accepts these sounds exactly as they are introduced; and a reasonably good radio receiver reproduces them faithfully. CW telegraphy cannot so discriminate. A dot is a dot,

14

and a dash is a dash. The only control over the note or tone of such characters is the one offered the *receiving* operator through adjustment of his various receiving controls. Regardless of the pitch or audio frequency, the tone will remain at that frequency unless the controls are readjusted. If approximately 400 cycles per second is the operator's choice of a pleasing tone, that's where he leaves his receiver settings; and each succeeding dot and dash will sound identical, frequencywise.

2-5. Now let's suppose that frequent bursts of static occur during a communication. Static electricity, as you learned in school, is a phenomenon of nature representing electrical disturbances (such as lightning) in free space. Lightning flashes, maybe not even visible at your receiving location, will nevertheless manifest themselves as a sudden, sharp crackling in your headphones or speaker. (The noise may be heard up to several hundred miles from the storm center.) Warning of such storms will often be evidenced in your radio receiver by a low, grumbling roll of variable intensity. Were you engaged in a radio*telephone* conversation, you would often lose a word, or several words perhaps. This either would destroy the intelligence of the communication and require a full repetition, or would involve a bit of guesswork on your part to try to patch in what you lost with the rest of the conversation.

2-6. With CW telegraphy, however, your chances are much better. You may lose a *letter* here and there, and sometimes even part of a word. Nevertheless, that is your only handicap; you do not also have to buck the inflections of the human voice! Everything you hear will be at the same steady audio tone (unless you jiggle your receiver controls).

2-7. Suppose we look further at this CW *versus* phone comparison. Phone is fun, because the speaker's personality is injected into the air lanes. You recognize the voice of an old friend, a loved one, or an exciting new contact. However, a radiophone channel occupies much more space, or width, in the radio-frequency assignments than a CW signal does. (You will learn more about radio frequency in later chapters.) Suffice it to say that—to take an arbitrary figure—as many as ten CW stations can operate simultaneously within the space in the radio spectrum required for one radiotelephone station. Scientific progress is doing much to narrow this spread. Nevertheless, CW still does—and no doubt will for some time to come—offer the advantage of sharp, well-defined limits within which their signals can be heard. With more than a quarter of a million amateurs operating in narrow bands internationally assigned them, it is readily apparent that the interference problem (one station overriding another) is far greater with phone than with CW.

2-8. All things being equal, CW and phone signals will travel equally as far. However, CW signals can be separated more easily in a receiver, and they are understandable even if weak and distorted. For this reason, they provide useful communication under circumstance which render phone useless. This means you can exchange intelligent communication with CW over much greater distances and with much less trouble than with phone. In other words, you will need much more power on phone to enjoy the same reliability which CW offers.

2-9. So much for phone *versus* CW. Arguments could be presented pro and con. However, regardless of what you think about it, you are going to *have* to learn the code—at least to the extent of five words per minute—or else you cannot become a legal amateur! And you do want to operate within the law, since heavy fines can be imposed on a person who flagrantly and habitually breaks the rules. Just as you could lose your license to drive a motor vehicle, so could you forfeit your radio license if you violate U.S. radio laws.

2-10. So, suppose we get into the serious business of discovering how you can learn the radio code. We are going to give you a few of the most practical and logical approaches. You aren't going to find it too difficult—and certainly not impossible. However, it *is* going to require that you put your mind to it and devote a reasonable amount of time to study and practice of the code each and every day.

2-11. Initially, when you have no previous knowledge of code characters and no partner with more experience, one of the automatic teaching devices is probably the most desirable. This doesn't mean you must lay out an impressive amount of "gold dust." The cost figures in amateur radio, regardless of whether you are a beginner or more advanced, are comparable to those of other popular hobbies, such as golf, archery, skin diving, etc. In ham radio, you can surround yourself with any number of elaborate contraptions; or you can accomplish the same end with more modest equipment.

2-12. If you have a tape recorder, magnetic tapes are available for about two or three dollars, from your radio, hi-fi, or music dealer. Incidentally, your radio and electronics parts dealer or distributor can be located in the yellow pages of your telephone directory under "Radio Supplies and Parts." Also available from your radio distributor are magnetic tapes on which code-practice lessons have been prerecorded. However, should you have a communications receiver, you can receive the automatic code-practice lessons sent by the many stations voluntarily devoted to this purpose, and make up your own practice tapes. You will need such a receiver when you go on the air anyway, so it is not a lost investment to procure one early in your code study.

2-13. A friendly ham neighbor—one who is willing to send code (provided he is a competent, experienced operator with a good "fist")—can make a tape recording for you, using an audio oscillator and hand key. Or he can easily make up a tape by using his own communications receiver, if you are not ready to invest in such equipment.

2-14. Lacking these items, you can ask your ham friend to send code practice to you on a hand key. A simple high-frequency buzzer, like the one in Fig. 2-3, is adequate where economy is a factor. The unit in Fig. 2-3 sells for under $5.00 and requires only a connection to a dry cell for operation. Code-practice sets of this

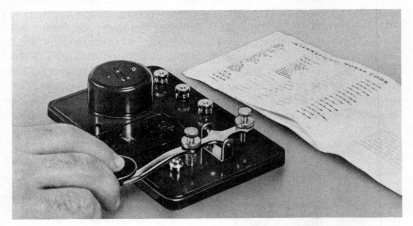

Courtesy E. F. Johnson Co.

Fig. 2-3. A battery-powered code-practice buzzer.

type are available at most radio parts distributors. Although the tone of a buzzer is somewhat scratchy at times, and inclined to change pitch occasionally, many an amateur has passed his radio code examination with no other training than that provided by a buzzer set. You can learn not only to receive with a buzzer set, but to send as well. An imported buzzer set which sells for under $3.00 is pictured in Fig. 2-4. The key from the buzzer can be used with your radio transmitter after you establish your station. If you prefer a higher-pitched note, the unit pictured in Fig. 2-5 can be purchased. This unit, available from Electropac, Inc., Peter-

Fig. 2-4. A small imported key-buzzer code-practice outfit.

borough, N.H., will operate from 6 to 28 volts DC. A 120-volt AC unit is also available. The DC unit sells for under $5.00.

2-15. As we have hinted previously, radio code is a series of sounds arranged in various combinations of short and long buzzes —or *dits* and *dahs*—separated by short spaces. Since there is no known method of printing such sounds, a substitute means was devised, whereby the various characters were indicated by printing dots and dashes in chart formation. Unfortunately, this encouraged beginners to learn the code by sight rather than by ear. Sounds are not seen; they are heard. Radio code reception is entirely a sound process, except in automatic high-speed tapes like those in Figs. 2-1 and 2-2. A completely superfluous mental process

Fig. 2-5. The *Sonalert* unit for producing a higher pitched note than that from a conventional buzzer.

Courtesy Electropac Inc.

was therefore introduced, in visualizing the code characters as printed dots and dashes and then attempting to associate them with their sounds. Some years ago, intense efforts were made to introduce code charts which represented dots and dashes by the expressions *dit* and *dah*. This served to reduce the mental effort involved and thus to speed up the code learning process. Although printed charts using the dot-and-dash interpretations are still

18

widely distributed, the *dit-dah* method is becoming increasingly popular. Modern texts are beginning to ignore anything other than printed *dit-dahs* for receiving training, which is the method we will use here. A combination dot-dash and *dit-dah* code chart is illustrated in Fig. 2-6. Note that only the alphabet and numerals are shown. After you have these down pat, make up your own *dit-dah* chart for punctuation and operating signals, using the chart in Fig. 2-7 as a guide. Notice that the alphabetical letter equivalents are shown in parentheses. Where a solid line appears

Letter and Number	International Morse Code	Phonic Sound
A	· —	di DAH
B	— · · ·	DAH di di dit
C	— · — ·	DAH di DAH dit
D	— · ·	DAH di dit
E	·	dit
F	· · — ·	di di DAH dit
G	— — ·	DAH DAH dit
H	· · · ·	di di di dit
I	· ·	di dit
J	· — — —	di DAH DAH DAH
K	— · —	DAH di DAH
L	· — · ·	di DAH di dit
M	— —	DAH DAH
N	— ·	DAH dit
O	— — —	DAH DAH DAH
P	· — — ·	di DAH DAH dit
Q	— — · —	DAH DAH di DAH
R	· — ·	di DAH dit
S	· · ·	di di dit
T	—	DAH
U	· · —	di di DAH
V	· · · —	di di di DAH
W	· — —	di DAH DAH
X	— · · —	DAH di di DAH
Y	— · — —	DAH di DAH DAH
Z	— — · ·	DAH DAH di dit
1	· — — — —	di DAH DAH DAH DAH
2	· · — — —	di di DAH DAH DAH
3	· · · — —	di di di DAH DAH
4	· · · · —	di di di di DAH
5	· · · · ·	di di di di dit
6	— · · · ·	DAH di di di dit
7	— — · · ·	DAH DAH di di dit
8	— — — · ·	DAH DAH DAH di dit
9	— — — — ·	DAH DAH DAH DAH dit
0	— — — — —	DAH DAH DAH DAH DAH

Fig. 2-6. Dot-and-dash and · dit-dah symbols for radiotelegraph code.

Symbols	Code
* From (DE)	— . . .
* End of Message ($\overline{\text{AR}}$)	. — . — .
* End of Work ($\overline{\text{SK}}$)	. . . — . —
* Wait ($\overline{\text{AS}}$)	. — . . .
* Invitation to Transmit (K)	— . —
* Error	. . . .
Understood	. . . — .
* Received OK (R)	. — .
* Period ($\overline{\text{AAA}}$)	. — . — . —
Semicolon	— . — . — .
Colon	— — — . . .
Comma	— — . . — —
Quotes	. — . . — .
* Question Mark ($\overline{\text{IMI}}$)	. . — — . .
Apostrophe	. — — — — .
Hyphen	— . . . . —
Fraction Bar	— . . — .
Parentheses	— . — — . —
Underscore	. . — — . —
* Double Dash (break) ($\overline{\text{BT}}$)	— . . . —
Per Cent	. — — — . — — .
Separation	. — . . —
* Attention ($\overline{\text{KA}}$)	— . — . —
* Indicates the symbols you must learn for your novice exam.	

Fig. 2-7. Punctuation and operating symbols.

above the character shown, the letters comprising it should be run together without spacing. You will find that, by puzzling them out yourself and by substituting the *dits* and *dahs* in Fig. 2-6 for the symbols in Fig. 2-7, you will almost automatically familiarize yourself with their phonic relationship to dots and dashes. You will encounter very few punctuation and operating signals in your novice exam. However, you *will* have a number of them to contend with in your on-the-air contacts; so, go ahead and learn them, too. You'll be that much better an operator.

2-16. As a beginner, think only in terms of *dits* and *dahs*. Study the sounds in the code chart (Fig. 2-6); and begin memorizing the *dits* and *dahs* by relating them to their associated letters.

figures, and punctuation. The letter *a*, for example, should be thought of as *dit-dah*—not as *dot-dash*. B is *dah-dit-dit-dit*, not *dash-dot-dot-dot*. The figure 6 becomes *dah-dit-dit-dit-dit*. Catch on?

2-17. Try it for yourself. Take the figure 8 on the code chart. Say it out loud, like this—*dah-dah-dah-dit-dit*. Do likewise with the letter *p*—*dit-dah-dah-dit*. Go through the whole chart the same way. Tomorrow, pick words from billboards, store signs—anywhere—and pronounce the letters in *dits* and *dahs*. Each day you will find yourself relating more and more of them to their associated *sounds* in code characters. Intersperse this kind of practice by listening to your tape-recorder lessons or by whatever other method you have chosen for your code practice.

2-18. Among the other devices available to you are automatic code transmitters which use paper tapes factory-punched with code-practice material. The Atko *Mini-Keyer* (Fig. 2-8), made by the Automatic Telegraph Keyer Corp., 275 Madison Ave., New York, N.Y. 10016, is an example of an automatic tape transmitter. This unit sells for less than $50.00. When you are finished with it, it has a good resale value to a radio club or an individual. Another type of automatic code transmitter can be purchased from the Instructograph Company of Chicago, Illinois, or Los Angeles, Cali-

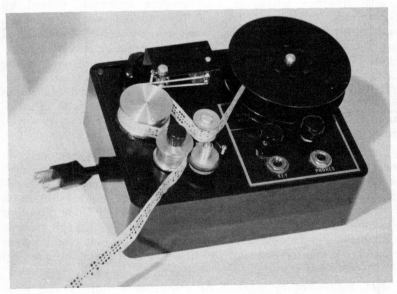

Fig. 2-8. The Atko *Mini-Keyer* automatic code transmitter.

fornia. This is a compact unit contained in a leatherette carrying case. It embodies not only a small motor which operates from your home lighting circuit, but also an audio oscillator and a speaker. The oscillator generates the signal you hear through the speaker (or headphones, if you don't want to disturb others in the room). The sound resembles that of an actual radio CW signal on the air. A series of ten paper tapes is provided, which offer a variety of code-practice characters, at speeds varying anywhere from 4 to 40 words per minute. The rate depends upon the tape and the speed at which you set the motor drive (which is continuously variable). This machine also costs in the neighborhood of fifty dollars. However, you can rent such a device from the manufacturer for about $4.50 per month. A nominal parcel post charge is made for transportation, which you must pay both ways. Not only does such a machine make receiving practice possible, but by connecting a hand telegraph key to the terminals provided, you can also engage in sending practice. You can supply your own key (and headphones, if desired) for the automatic transmitter, or rent both of them with the equipment. However, both key and phones will be necessities in your station when you go on the air. A standard key, fully adjustable, will serve you well with your practice set and actual transmitter when you begin operations.

2-19. Another automatic code-sending machine, offered by Gardiner & Company of Stratford, New Jersey, is small, compact, and light in weight. It, too, uses the factory-punched, double-sided paper tape. Ten rolls, containing twenty practice lessons, are included. This little device sells for about $32.00 postpaid in the United States. Unlike the other machine, it does not incorporate a built-in oscillator or speaker. (This unit is of no particular value to those who already own such equipment.) This type of automatic sender will, of course, perform with a battery-powered buzzer set as well as with a code oscillator.

2-20. You are by no means limited to any one device for code learning. In addition to automatic code transmitting machines, pre-recorded code-practice lessons are available on magnetic recording tape. These tapes can be puchased from most radio parts distributors. The Howard W. Sams *International Code Training System* consists of a series of three 33⅓-rpm phonograph records with 30 recorded exercises. They contain the code at gradually increasing speeds, which take the ham aspirant from the start up to 22 words per minute.

2-21. Still another method of acquiring radiotelegraph code ability is available. As previously explained, a communications receiver will provide plenty of on-the-air training. Whether you pick up a piece of surplus military gear (often available at surplus stores, at prices ranging from five dollars up), a second-hand commercial ham receiver, or a brand-new piece of equipment, is up to you and your pocketbook. The average price of a good used ham receiver is in the neighborhood of $150. For that figure you can frequently pick up one which originally sold for $300. However, you *can* spend as high as $1,200 to $1,500 on new equipment, if you so desire. If you are completely green to ham radio, we most certainly recommend that you take a more experienced ham with you when you choose a receiver. Your judicious choice initially of a *good* receiver can guarantee you many pleasant hours of *QSO*, or communication with other stations. Pick a poor receiver and your frustration will be infinite!

2-22. Remember, in choosing a receiver, that you are buying a more or less permanent piece of equipment for your eventual station. Maybe you later will want to buy the finest equipment available. As an average novice, however, you will first want the best for the least cost. Check the many radio distributors in your area and take with you an experienced ham operator who knows the type of equipment you will need. His many years of knowledge and experience in the field can be a big help to you in selecting the proper equipment whether it be in kit form or factory wired.

2-23. And now, why practice with a receiver? With it, you will hear actual radio signals through your headphones or speaker. (You will find it much easier to learn code, as well as to use it, if you stick to the headphones and forget the speaker.) However, listening to actual radio signals can be of little help unless you know what to listen to. For example, let's suppose that you tune in a commercial marine radio shore station which calls the roll of ships on the high seas for whom it has message traffic. To you— a novice aspirant—such transmissions will be a meaningless jumble of *dits* and *dahs*. You can't even read them; they come too fast for a beginner. If you're smart, you'll ignore this type of signal and tune in one of the regular code-practice stations. You didn't know they existed? Well, they most certainly do! That famous international organization of radio amateurs, the American Radio Relay League, Inc., takes good care of that. Their own memorial station, W1AW (a tribute to the late Hiram Percy Maxim, who, in collaboration with his younger associate, Clarence D. Tuska, founded the ARRL in 1914), sends code-practice transmissions on a regular schedule and on various frequencies throughout the year. These transmissions will provide you with much valuable code practice. Supplementing this are many code-practice transmissions, which are made at regularly scheduled times and on definite selected frequencies by volunteer member stations of the ARRL. Other services provide similar code-practice sessions. They are yours to listen to—and for free! For a complete, up-to-the-minute schedule of these various transmissions, just write the American Radio Relay League, 225 Main St., Newington, Connecticut. The league will supply you with complete information on such code-practice transmissions, at no cost.

2-24.   To listen to the transmissions of *novice* stations will be more of a liability than an asset! Sure, it's the novice class which you are aspiring to enter—but don't forget that novice means "apprentice," and apprentice means beginner! In other words, the formation of code characters (known in the operating profession as a "fist") by a novice will be hesitant and stumbling. It will not be the firm, solid transmission of the more experienced amateur or professional. You will be tempted to write down what such stations send because their transmissions will be in the speed class your are striving to enter—in other words, five words per minute. *Don't* do it! Far better that you stick to the perfect machine sending of W1AW, or one of its volunteer stations scattered between the coasts. Their character formation is exactly in accord with International radiotelegraph code. That is, *dits* are identical in length; *dahs* are three times as long as *dits*. Spaces between *letters* (or characters) are one *dit* long; those between words are exactly three *dits* long (the same as a *dah*). This is the type of transmission which will give you the needed practice, and most rapidly increase your ability to recognize the proper formation of the code characters.

2-25.   Another common mistake of most beginners is to tune in a station that is sending at a speed which permits solid copy. By "solid copy" we mean a speed of transmission which enables you to write down *every single letter* transmitted, without error. By such procedure, you learn exactly nothing! You have no challenge . . . nothing to reach for. Once you can copy solid at five words per minute, try to copy a transmission at eight or ten words a minute. Concentrate! Get every bit you can at a speed just *beyond* your solid-copy ability. The automatic challenge thus provided will raise your code speed beyond the requirements for the novice license in a much shorter time than if you were to listen to something you could interpret 100 per cent.

2-26.   "Should we write it?" you ask. Definitely *yes*! Experienced operators seldom write down everything they hear. On the other hand, to carry a conversation in your head is quite a trick, radiowise! Therefore, *write* what you hear during your novice year. After you've gained experience, you'll find that much of the chatter you indulge in on the air lanes can be received and registered in your brain, and the intelligence extracted, merely by listening as you would to a face-to-face or telephone conversation. If you find that you can handle a two-way conversation without writing down what the other person has to say, fine. However, don't feel at all embarrassed if you have to record your conversations for the first few months, letter for letter and word for word— you'll have a lot of company!

2-27. Learning to receive means practice, and lots of it. Despite many scientific attempts to develop a quick and easy method of acquiring a working knowledge of the radiotelegraph code, there *is* no "easy" way. It still is a matter of practice, more practice, and even *more* practice! Moreover, the effort expended in learning the radiotelegraph code will pay you back many times. Remember though—the mere fact that you can interpret the hieroglyphics of radio codes does *not* mean you are an operator. You're also going to have to know how to talk back. In radiotelegraphy, this simply means you must know how to manipulate a telegraph key. If you've never watched a CW ham operating, you surely must have noticed the operator in the railroad depot who "wiggles a bug" or works a key to produce the characters of the Morse code. If he is on the sending end, he has to make intelligible movements of his key so that they can be understood by the receiving operator. So must you, too, as a prospective amateur radio novice, learn to formulate the characters of the radiotelegraph code so that the receiving operator can interpret them. Otherwise, you'll have no contact with other radio hams.

2-28. Some say that learning to send is much simpler than learning to receive. Be that as it may (it varies with the individual), the better character formation you learn to make on the key, the more answers you will receive. In most manuals which attempt to teach you how to send and receive, you'll find much emphasis placed upon how you hold the key knob. Actually, it makes little difference! Hold the knob in whichever manner feels most comfortable to you. All this hullabaloo about "place the right third finger on the right-hand rim of the key knob, the right thumb on the left-hand rim, the right forefinger lightly on the upper surface of the knob" is, in fact, nonsense. Certainly you can send that way; you can also send, to a certain extent, by using your left foot! The whole object in character formation on a telegraph key is to grasp the knob in the most comfortable fashion. The British, Japanese, and others use a key with a "door-knob" type of finger knob. Some of them grab it as if they were drawing water from a well; others climb right on top of it with a delicate finger movement. Regardless of *how* they hold the knob, most of them turn out some pretty good code transmission.

2-29. Carefully examine Fig. 2-9. It shows the conventional grip used by 90 per cent of the experienced amateurs today. Try positioning your fingers and thumb that way first. Be sure the key is back far enough (18 inches is a good distance) that the muscle under your forearm rests on top of the table. Keep your fingers loose! Don't tense up and hold the key as though it might run away. If you have trouble relaxing your fingers, hold a small

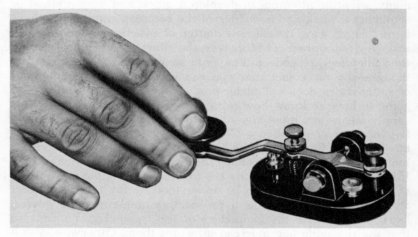

Fig. 2-9. Conventional grip used in operating a hand telegraph key.

wad of paper, a plum, small orange, or a small rubber ball in your palm while sending. This will keep your fingers rounded, and reduce the tendency to stiffen up. If this position seems comfortable and you feel you can make good character formation, then by all means practice sending in this fashion. However, do not feel duty-bound to adopt this position initially. If it feels awkward so that your characters are more hesitant and fumbling than with another hold which gives you more confidence, use your own interpretation. After you have acquired a reasonable ability in forming the characters, check your grip again. We'll wager that you have changed a bit and are approaching the conventional hold (Fig. 2-9), if you haven't already adopted it in full!

2-30. We've discussed several methods of learning code by means of such automatic devices as magnetic tapes, factory-punched paper tape on automatic transmitters, phonograph records, and even the elementary key-buzzer-battery combination. However, you aren't through yet! We casually mentioned the audio oscillator earlier in this chapter. This device—which represents a cross between the more elaborate automatic code-practice sets and the buzzer affair—is worthy of your most careful consideration. An audio oscillator (Fig. 2-10) produces oscillations at a frequency audible to the human ear. This signal, produced within the unit itself, is reproduced in the headphones or speaker. These oscillations are not subject to interference from other radiations, such as the ones encountered in a receiver. Likewise, their frequency or pitch will not change, as frequently happens with the

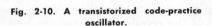
Fig. 2-10. A transistorized code-practice oscillator.

Courtesy Allied Radio Corp.

more modest buzzer practice sets. The tone will be pure, pleasant, and steady. In some units, the tone and volume can be varied widely, enabling you to secure the most pleasing tone or note. Like a buzzer set, the audio oscillator will reproduce characters formed by either a manual key or an automatic keying device. By using the audio oscillator, you can practice sending to your heart's content and be assured that a continuously pleasant tone will be produced.

2-31. Audio oscillators are offered by a number of manufacturers. They are available in various types, with or without speakers. For example, an audio code-practice oscillator with a built-in speaker usually costs about sixteen dollars; a comparable model without the integral speaker sells at a lower price. These units can be used later in your on-the-air amateur station, as a radio-frequency monitor—an added refinement which greatly increases operating convenience.

2-32. Other oscillators feature a combination radio-frequency monitor and code-practice oscillator; however, it may not include

27

a built-in speaker. Such a unit costs a little less than twenty dollars. Another unit employs a code-practice oscillator/monitor with built-in speaker; it sells for about fifteen dollars. More recently introduced was a small transistor code-practice oscillator and monitor which costs around six dollars. It operates entirely from penlite cells, but produces headphone volume. Many of these units can be purchased in kit form. This will represent a savings to you, as well as a chance to actually assemble some of your own equipment. Parts are available at your radio parts distributor.

2-33. We've taken you through the necessity for learning the code, the equipment you will need to do so, and the methods of acquiring this proficiency. We would like to add that neither you nor anyone else can become a five-word-per-minute operator—as required by the novice examination—by merely reading the previous paragraphs, purchasing the necessary equipment, and sitting down for an hour or so. You should be willing to devote about thirty hours toward practicing the radiotelegraph code. Intersperse this practice with a study of the requirements for the written examination. You should be ready for the examination within the thirty hours. However, you'll be that much *more* ready if you give thirty hours to code and twenty to the written portion.

2-34. Don't try to learn it all at once! Anything requiring the mental concentration that learning the code demands is a strain. Remember, being a ham is a hobby. A hobby is something *you* ride! When *it* rides you, it becomes a chore.

2-35. Take your code in small doses. Study the paragraphs pertaining to the written portion of the examination a few at a time. Relax between study sessions. After you have your second wind, "fire up" the automatic tape transmitter, the record player, or the communications receiver again. Not for long, though. A half hour of *dits* and *dahs* can be too long if you're tired. You won't gain anything by prolonging your practice until it becomes agony.

2-36. If you are a teen-ager, you probably can learn faster than the older novices. However, don't beat yourself to death trying to learn it all before the sun goes down. Take your time; do the job thoroughly and do it right.

2-37. By now you should have a pretty clear picture of what the code is all about. Suppose, for the time being, that we forget about the code, and get on with the written material. You should come back to the code portion from time to time, until you have completely mastered it, at a minimum of five words per minute. Alternate one with the other, and before you know it you will be ready for the novice examination.

3

Basic Electricity

3-1. Electricity is a big subject. Probably more has been written about it and its many ramifications than about any other science. Fortunately for the aspirant to a radio amateur novice license, only the most basic knowledge of electricity is required. For those of you who have studied high-school physics, this chapter will constitute a review, and should be thoroughly studied so that you can refresh your memory.

3-2. We will be concerned with several words in the terminology of electrical values and equipment. Many of these—such as voltage, amperes, etc.—have become household terms. Your toaster uses 115 volts . . . your car battery is charging at so many amps. These words roll off your tongue like water down a drain. But do you know what they mean? We have provided a glossary of commonly used electrical terms and their meanings in the Appendix at the back of the book. Whenever you run across terminology which puzzles you in the text, refer to the Glossary, so that you can fully grasp the meaning of the sentence in which it occurs. We will commence by clarifying the most commonly used term—voltage—together with an explanation of several sources from which it is supplied.

3-3. Voltage (named after the eminent scientist Volta) is the *force* or *pressure* which causes *current* to flow in an electrical circuit. You will understand this better by referring to Fig. 3-1. You have pressure in your water pipes. This pressure is always present, but is not released until you open a valve or faucet, as shown in Fig. 3-1A. Think, then, in terms of pressure when you are considering voltage. Such pressure is always present in *batteries*. It is stored chemically in the battery cells, ready for release the instant "an electrical valve (switch) is turned on," or, in electrical terms, when a circuit is completed (Fig. 3-1B). Electrically you have "turned on the valve" when you close the switch.

3-4. Likewise, *voltage* is present in a generator, alternator, or dynamotor. Contrary to the battery (wet or dry)—in which the voltage is always present in chemical form, ready for instant release upon completion of the circuit—the generator, alternator, or dynamotor does not produce a voltage *until* rotated mechanically. When any of these devices is rotating at its normal rated speed, our friend "Mr. Voltage" is present, asking only that you

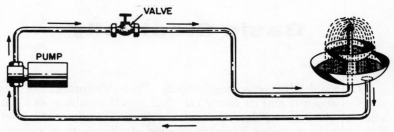

(A) Water current cannot flow until the valve is turned on.

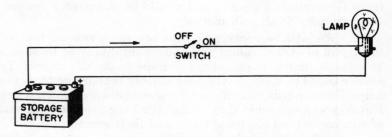

(B) Electrical current cannot flow until the switch is turned on.

Fig. 3-1. There must be a complete circuit before current can flow.

close the circuit to benefit from his actions. Several common sources of voltage are illustrated in Fig. 3-2.

3-5. What does voltage do? Suppose we go back to the water-pressure analogy. What does your water pressure do when you open a valve or faucet? Normally, water begins to flow through the pipes. The rate of flow depends upon the amount of *pressure*, as well as upon the size of the pipe. Voltage, likewise, is the pressure which pushes current through a wire. The proper technical term for this voltage, or pressure, is *electromotive force*, abbreviated *emf*. (This term appears frequently in electrical texts.) So much for voltage at this time. Just remember that it's the push which makes the current flow.

3-6. What is this *current* that flows as a result of the shove the voltage gives it? Current is to electricity what water is to your

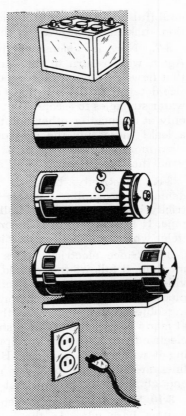

(A) Storage battery.

(B) Dry cell.

(C) Automobile generator.

(D) Dynamotor.

(E) Household wall outlet.

Fig. 3-2. Common sources of voltage.

hydraulic system—the medium which does the job. Where water is measured in gallons, current is measured in *amperes* (named for an early experimenter, Ampère). It may be likened again to water in that both are substances. Water is visible, whereas electrical current is not. Nevertheless, each is a substance which is moved through a conducting medium (pipe for water, wire for electrical current) from a source of pressure (pump or gravity for water, voltage for electricity) in order to perform a certain function. Although both designations—gallons for water, amperes for electrical current—represent quantity, the *absolute* measure of electrical quantity is the *coulomb*. Don't let such a complex term scare you; it merely means that if one coulomb flows in one second, the resultant *current* is one *ampere*. We mention coulombs only because you *may* be asked, "what is the electrical unit of quantity?" The correct answer would be *coulombs*. Although it is

31

doubtful whether you will encounter it in your novice examination, tuck the term away in the back of your mind.

3-7. Now let's consider the next basic element—*resistance*. Again we'll return to the water analogy. The *amount* of water that flows through a pipe depends upon the *size* of the pipe. The size determines the *resistance* of the pipe to the water's flow. The water struggles to escape from the pipe. You want it to escape, but only at a faucet or other point where it can be put to use, not as a leak! Increasing the pressure of a water-supply system puts even more strain on the pipe. The pressure can be increased beyond the safe pressure limit, at which point the pipe will burst!

3-8. Electricity, being in many ways analogous to water, demonstrates similar characteristics. However, unlike water, electricity does *not* require a hollow conducting medium, such as a pipe. It is made up of *electrons*. These are minute invisible particles which will be discussed in more detail later.

3-9. Since electricity does not require a *hollow* conducting medium, it follows that a *solid* means of conduction must be provided. This explains why electricity is conducted in wires, not in pipes or tubes. Such conductors must be insulated from surrounding objects and surfaces. Otherwise, electricity would leak off at many points, and create a shock hazard. However, the farmer's electric fence uses bare wire purposely, so that any animal touching it will receive a shock. High-voltage electrical transmission lines are generally bare for reasons of economy, but are high enough above the ground that they are not hazardous.

3-10. Some of the radio-frequency circuits in transmitters also contain bare wire. In the higher-powered transmitters, hollow metallic (usually copper) tubing is frequently used. The high-frequency currents do *not* flow through the hollow space in the tubing. A peculiarity of currents at these extremely high frequencies is that they travel on the outer *surface* of the conductor (even in a solid conductor). This condition is known as *skin effect*. Thus, tubing can supply the same usable surface area, at less cost and weight, as a solid conductor with the same outside diameter.

3-11. Solid wire also introduces some resistance to the current (amperes pushed by volts). Of all the baser metals, copper offers the least resistance. Hence, practically all wiring—in your home, in motor windings and transformers, and in industry—is of copper. Silver, platinum, and a few other precious metals offer slightly less resistance; but the gain is insufficient to offset their higher cost. Small quantities of the rarer metals, such as silver and platinum, are used for sensitive relay contacts and similar specialized applications.

3-12. We will confine our discussion to copper wire, since it is the accepted standard. As previously mentioned, it also has a certain resistance to the flow of electricity, just as pipe and hose have for water. Such resistance, aggravated by overloading, will actually manifest itself in heat (whether in a pipe or wire). Heat is generated when a water pipe is subjected to a higher-than-normal water pressure. However, this heat cannot be felt because the water and the larger metal area of the pipe quickly dissipate it. Above-normal pressure can be felt as heat on the surface of an air hose; even normal pressure will make it warm. Ever feel the tires on your car after a long, high-speed drive in hot weather? Friction between the tires and the hot pavement increases the pressure in the tire, producing heat. Carried to extremes, your tires could blow out! Likewise, attempting to push too many amperes of current through a wire which is too small to accommodate them will result in heat. This heat can be easily felt on the outer surface of the insulation. A short circuit (wherein the voltage pushes an abnormal amount of current through the wire) can, and often does, burn the insulation. The wire itself may even melt, which explains a great many electrical fires. (A melted wire is equivalent to a water pipe or air hose that has burst because of excessive pressure.) For this reason, electrical fuses and the more modern thermal circuit breaker (which can be restored after it has "kicked out") were developed. A fuse is nothing more than a short length of wire with a *lower* melting point than that of the copper wire to which it is connected. Should the current become excessive, the fuse wire will melt and thereby prevent any further current flow.

3-13. Whereas the size of water pipe, copper tubing, and similar hollow-core conductors is rated in cross-sectional *inches*, wiring in electrical circuits has a different method of sizing. The most popular system in the United States is the American Wire Gauge (AWG), formerly known as Browne and Sharpe (B & S). Certain numerical designations are assigned to the various sizes of wire. Likewise, each wire size has a specified maximum safe carrying capacity in amperes. For example, the most common wiring for *lighting* circuits in your home is No. 14; its *maximum* safe carrying capacity is 15 amperes.* For the appliance outlets (commonly but erroneously referred to as "wall plugs"), No. 12 wire is generally used. Larger than the No. 14, it has a maximum safe carrying capacity of 20 amperes.* Note that the larger the wire, the smaller the number. Larger wiring is used in the appliance circuits because a toaster, waffle iron, or juice mixer requires

---

* In cables or conduit; in open wiring, 5 amperes more.

more current than the light bulbs do. The larger wire insures that its *resistance* to the current will not be great enough to cause heat unless an abnormal number of appliances are used simultaneously.

3-14. The same holds true with heavier-duty items, such as an electric range. Considerable current is required to heat an oven and one or more burners. Obviously, this calls for a larger wire size than where toasters, food mixers, and the like are the only concern. Let's suppose that, at maximum demand (oven and all four burners on full), the electric range requires 45 amperes of current, under a pressure of 115 volts. We have just seen that No. 12 wire has a safe carrying capacity of 20 amperes. Obviously, if the range were supplied from a 115-volt pressure source through No. 12 wire, the wire would be overloaded more than 100%! So, to decrease the resistance and consequent heating effect, a larger wire would be required. We find that No. 6 wire in cable or conduit will safely handle 55 amperes continuously. It, then, with a pressure of 115 volts, would handle the electric range, with a good safety factor. However, No. 6 wire is rather large. In fact, it is about four times the size of No. 12!

3-15. So, since *current*—not *voltage*—determines the wire size, let's briefly examine an electrical device known as a *transformer*. A transformer contains two coils. (Sometimes it contains more than two, but for ease of explanation, we will consider the simplest type.) One coil is known as the *primary*; the other, the *secondary*. Fig. 3-3 illustrates several types of transformers. If the secondary has *more* turns than the primary, the voltage will be stepped up, or increased. If the secondary has *less* turns, the voltage will be stepped down, or decreased. Sounds good, doesn't it? Apparently, all we need do is step up the voltage anytime we need more volts. Unfortunately, the laws of nature say that "something's got to give." Sure, we can increase the *voltage*. In the process, we lose *current*. In other words, when the voltage is stepped up by the transformer in Fig. 3-4A, the amount of current is *decreased* proportionately. Conversely, in a step-down transformer (Fig. 3-4B), the voltage is lowered, but there is a proportional *increase* in the current. Transformers designed for heavy-duty operation are given a power rating. Power is rated in *watts*, which can be found by multiplying the voltage (in volts) by the current (in amperes). From Fig. 3-4 you will notice that the wattage, or power, handled by the primary and secondary windings (in either the step-up or step-down transformer) is the same. Only the ratio between the voltage and current has been changed. (Wattage will be discussed later in more detail.) Suppose, through use of a suitable transformer, the voltage is doubled, or stepped up, from 115 to 230 volts.

(A) Power transformers.

(B) Audio-output transformer.

(C) Combined plate and filament transformer.

Fig. 3-3. Typical transformers.

Increasing the voltage (pressure) reduces the current in direct proportion, in order to supply the same amount of power in watts. Therefore, were we to supply a range with 230 volts, only *half* of the initially determined *current* of 45 amperes would be required. If the current requirements were cut in half and the voltage

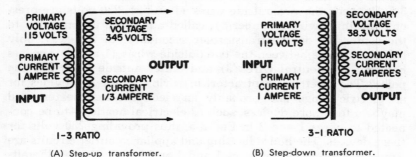

PRIMARY VOLTAGE 115 VOLTS	SECONDARY VOLTAGE 345 VOLTS
PRIMARY CURRENT 1 AMPERE	**OUTPUT**
INPUT	SECONDARY CURRENT 1/3 AMPERE

1-3 RATIO

(A) Step-up transformer.

PRIMARY VOLTAGE 115 VOLTS	SECONDARY VOLTAGE 38.3 VOLTS
INPUT	SECONDARY CURRENT 3 AMPERES
PRIMARY CURRENT 1 AMPERE	**OUTPUT**

3-1 RATIO

(B) Step-down transformer.

Fig. 3-4. Transformer action.

doubled, the range would operate on No. 12 wire. But there would be a slight heating effect! Why? Because No. 12 wire is rated to carry 20 amperes continuously, whereas the demand—although cut in half—is still 22.5 amperes, or slightly over the rated *safe* carrying capacity of No. 12 wire. Such a slight overload *might* not give any trouble, since the range seldom operates at full capacity. Nevertheless, No. 12 wire might be dangerous. The wire is continuously resisting the extra 2.5-ampere load being placed on it under full-load conditions. Such resistance manifests itself in heat. (The outer surface of the insulation on the wire will feel slightly warm.) Besides, the range will not be operating at peak efficiency because the full 22.5 amperes are not being used in the oven and burners—2.5 amperes are being consumed in heating the wire, in its effort to accommodate the current which the voltage is pushing at it. So, to play it safe, let's examine the problem a bit further. The next wire size above No. 12 is No. 10, rated at a safe carrying capacity of 30 amperes. Ah, we're getting somewhere—a 7.5-ampere safety factor. However, let's not split hairs. Many electric ranges are bigger hogs than you think. Their current consumption on full load *could* (and often does) exceed even the 30-ampere capacity of No. 10 wire. Let's look at No. 8 wire. With its rated current-carrying capacity of 40 amperes, it is as large as you will need for the average electric range. A current of 22.5 to 30 amperes (or even more) through a wire rated to accommodate 40 amperes will leave the insulation on the wire cool. By getting all the current it requires, the range will thus operate at peak efficiency. The current-carrying capacity is adequate to overcome whatever resistance the wire might offer, without wasting current in heating the wire instead of the burners. The 230 volts? The power company ordinarily supplies this 230 volts directly from a transformer located on a utility pole near the home. Contrary to the two-wire service used in earlier days, today most homes have *three* wires feeding the house, as shown in Fig. 3-5. Between the two outside wires (1 and 2), 230 volts are present; the third wire (number 3), called a neutral, is connected to the center tap on the transformer secondary. In this way, only half the voltage between the two outside wires (1 and 2) appears between the neutral wire (3) and either outside wire. See the point? The electrical contractor, in wiring a house, provides for an electric range and probably an electric water heater—and maybe a few more devices, such as electrical heating—to be connected to wires 1 and 2 in Fig. 3-5, thus providing 230 volts for these devices. The house lighting and appliance outlet circuits are connected across either wires 1 and 3 or 2 and 3, giving 115 volts for small appliances and illumination. Standard practice is to

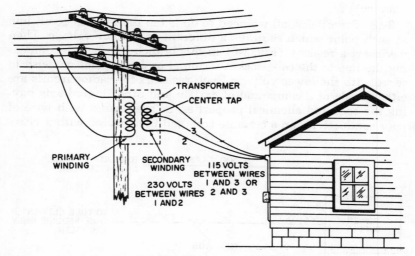

Fig. 3-5. A three-wire, 230-volt connection to the home.

balance the load by connecting approximately half the lighting and appliance circuits between the neutral wire (3) and one outside wire, and the other half between the neutral and other outside wire.

3-16. Let's get back to resistance. It is desirable in certain applications, undesirable in others. We can't dismiss it, however; it's here to stay. But we *can* and *do* take advantage of it in many ways. Numerous electrical appliances—such as toasters, percolators, and heaters—find resistance a great asset. In radio equipment, we are going to have to accept some *undesirable* resistance, which may occur here and there throughout our circuits without giving us anything in return. But we are going to pull a sneak and take much more advantage of the many places where resistance is really an asset! Let's see how and where. Right now is a good time to tell you that the unit of resistance is an *ohm*; you'll need to know that for your exam.

3-17. The internal elements (plate, screen, etc.) of the electron tubes in our radio transmitter require a relatively high-voltage direct current for operation. (You will learn more about plates and screens in a later chapter.) A figure of 500 volts DC is about right for the plate of the final amplifier tube, within the power limitations authorized for novice operation. The source of the 500 volts is called a *power supply*, which we will discuss in the next chapter. We now have the 500 volts needed. But where would we get, for example, 250 or so volts for the tube elements that require a lower voltage? This is where we take advantage of resistance!

3-18. Essentially, all we need to do is tap the main 500-volt line at each point which requires a different and lesser voltage. Then we insert a resistor (Fig. 3-6) in this branch line before connecting the line to the tube-socket terminal or other point we wish to serve with the lower voltage. Such resistors for radio circuits are either made of a compound of carbon and other ingredients having the required chemical properties, or are wound with wire of poor conductivity on a ceramic core and then coated with a vitre-

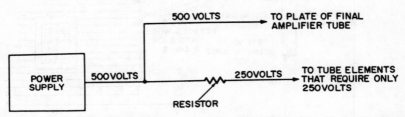

Fig. 3-6. Reducing the voltage to the proper value by inserting a resistor in the circuit.

ous enamel. Either the carbon or the wirewound type of resistor will *resist* the flow of curent, causing a voltage drop. The amount of drop and the resultant voltage which appears after the current passes through the resistor depend upon the chemical makeup of the carbon resistor—or, for the wirewound resistor, the size, type, and amount of resistance wire used. The carbon type (Fig. 3-7A) is customarily used in circuits where only a little current is required to pass through it. For the larger current demand, the wirewound type (Fig. 3-7B) is employed.

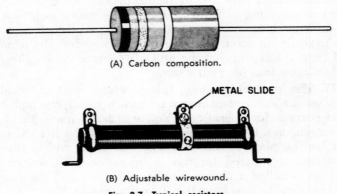

(A) Carbon composition.

(B) Adjustable wirewound.

Fig. 3-7. Typical resistors.

3-19. Connecting a resistor of the proper value in series with a particular element provides the lower voltages required. However, to attain better regulation—that is, the margin between "no load" (transmitting key up or "open") and "full load" (key down or "closed")—a voltage-divider resistor (or resistors) is commonly used. A voltage divider is simply a string of carbon resistors or a single wirewound type connected between the positive high-voltage, direct-current source and the negative source. Such a resistor, if of the wirewound type, is usually fitted with one or more metal sliders (Fig. 3-7B). These sliders can be moved along a bared portion of the resistance wire and mechanically secured at whatever points provide the desired voltages. A number of voltages can thus be obtained. When carbon resistors are used, the required resistance must be calculated. A string of two or more resistors, depending upon how many voltages are required, can be connected in series (that is, end to end); the branch lines are then taken off at the proper points between the resistors, as shown in Fig. 3-8.

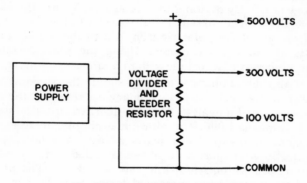

Fig. 3-8. A voltage-divider network.

3-20. Used in this way, a resistor has a dual purpose. It serves not only as a voltage divider, but also as a bleeder resistor (which it is often called). It is connected directly across the positive and negative high-voltage wires, causing a small amount of current to constantly pass through it as long as power is being supplied to the transmitter. (By "small" we mean a fraction of an ampere.) This bleeding action, in addition to providing better voltage regulation, also is a most desirable safety feature, as you will learn when we discuss power supplies.

3-21. Before leaving basic electricity, we will elaborate on one more item vital to amateur operation. This is the electrical unit of power called the *watt*; it also derives its name from an early experimenter, James Watt. A *watt* is the amount of power in a circuit when a *pressure* of one *volt* causes a *current* of one *ampere* to flow. The power law states that:

$$\text{volts} \times \text{amperes} = \text{watts}$$

Memorize this formula, because you will use it constantly in amateur radio. Your chief interest will be centered on the direct-current wattage consumed in supplying power to the plate of the final-amplifier tube in your transmitter. Novices are legally limited to a power of 75 watts input to the plate circuit of the final amplifier tube. We will go into plate current and watts input in a later chapter.

3-22. To assist you in better understanding watts, think of your household appliances. Your toaster, for example, probably carries a nameplate which (among other data) rates the appliance at 850 watts and the voltage at 115. Once these two values are known, it is simple to determine the amount of current in amperes which will be required at a voltage of 115 to produce the 850 watts of power required by the toaster. Let's see. You know the wattage; the voltage is 115. By dividing the voltage (115) into the 850 watts, you come up with a current requirement of slightly over 7 amperes. Now look at your electric iron; it is probably rated at about 660 watts at 115 volts. Current? Using the same formula, you arrive at a current of a little less than 6 amperes. Simple, isn't it?

3-23. With such appliances as ranges and others requiring more than 1,000 watts each, it is customary to refer to their power requirements in *kilo*watts. As you learned in school science classes, *kilo* means 1,000. Therefore, it is simpler to refer to 1,000 watts as one kilowatt, 5,000 watts as five kilowatts, etc. Frequently, a 250-watt ham transmitter is called a quarter-kilowatt transmitter; 500 watts, a half-kilowatt, and so on. The prefix *kilo* can be extended to other electrical terms as well. For instance, 1,000 volts is correctly called a kilovolt, and 5,000 volts, 5 kilovolts. Since the average ham transmitter is rated at less than 1,000 volts, this term is rarely used.

3-24. You will also find the prefix *milli*, which is a common term in radio measurement, both in amateur and professional applications. The word *milli* means one thousandth. For amateur work, it is also invariably associated with current. Although the voltage is relatively high in ham radio transmitters (500 to 1,000 volts), the current is low. Seldom is one ampere found at any point in the radio circuits (except in the highest-powered transmitters). The average novice transmitter, which is permitted a maximum power input of 75 watts to the final amplifier tube, is generally supplied with about 500 volts. Using the formula we tried before, you will come up with 0.15 ampere—or fifteen one-hundredths of one ampere. A higher-powered station of the general class may use 500 watts, or one-half kilowatt; the plate voltage is perhaps 1,500. By again working out the formula, you'll find that, even with so much power, the current required is only 0.33 ampere—or a third of one ampere!

3-25. For this reason, the currents in the radio circuits of transmitters are commonly referred to in *milliamperes*, each milliampere representing one one-thousandth of an ampere. It can readily be seen that the novice station using 0.15 ampere is drawing 150 milliamperes, the larger station with a 0.33-ampere demand is drawing 330 milliamperes. In their jargon, hams go one step farther and simply say 150 "mils" or 330 "mils"—or, if written, 150 ma or 330 ma.

3-26. That does it! You've waded through a lot of principles and terms having to do with the fundamentals of electricity. Actually, we've just scratched the surface. But since you are going to be a novice radio amateur, *not* an electrical engineer, this is all the information you'll need. In fact, we have given you more than enough. Understand that whatever you are asked in the examination will be only a small fraction of what we have given you; but not knowing which questions you may be confronted with, you must be familiar with *all* of them. At the same time, you're getting a good running start on your future examination for the higher-grade licenses, as well as an appreciation of what your radio transmitter is all about. Shall we try your skill now with several sample questions?

1. A volt is the unit of:
    (a) quantity (b) pressure (c) resistance (d) power
                                    ANSWER: (b).

2. Electrical resistance is rated in:
    (a) ohms (b) volts (c) amperes (d) watts   ANSWER: (a).

3. Wattage is the term used to describe:
    (a) power (b) quantity (c) pressure (d) volume ANSWER: (a).

This question could trip you, because (b) and (d) mean essentially the same. Both are wrong, of course!

4. A kilowatt is:
    (a) 100 watts (b) 10 watts (c) 1,000 watts (d) 500 watts
                                      ANSWER: (c).

5. Currents of less than one ampere are commonly referred to as:

   (a) kiloamperes   (b) milliwatts   (c) microvolts   (d) milliamperes

   ANSWER: (d).

6. Resistance has the property of:

   (a) opposing   (b) assisting   (c) increasing   (d) flowing

   ANSWER: (a).

7. A current of 10 amperes at a pressure of 100 volts represents what amount of power in watts?

   (a) 10   (b) 0.1   (c) 1,000   (d) 0.001   ANSWER: (c).

8. A novice transmitter, limited by law to a plate power input of 75 watts, uses 500 volts on the plate of the final amplifier tube. What value of current may be used as a maximum without exceeding the legal power limit?

   (a) 75 ma   (b) 100 ma   (c) 500 ma   (d) 150 ma   ANSWER: (d).

Remember the formula and put it in reverse. Divide 500 into 75 thinking in terms of milliamperes!

9. Alternating current can be stepped either up or down by a:

   (a) voltage divider   (b) bleeder resistor   (c) transformer   (d) swinging choke.   ANSWER: (c).

And if you change something, you "transform" it to something else! See?

4

Radio Power Supplies

4-1. Neither radio transmission nor reception would be possible without some source of electrical power. Modern radio tubes require power to heat their filaments. The plates and screens of the tubes also require power. Even the little transistor needs power, if only an insignificant amount from a tiny flashlight battery.

4-2. A fixed* amateur radio station requires two kinds of power. One is alternating current, which operates your household appliances and lights. The other is direct current, like that supplied by your car battery and generator. Direct current alone will power a radio transmitter and receiver. However, alternating current from the appliance outlets is far more convenient and much cheaper for operating your station in your home.

4-3. The most practical power source for a mobile installation in a car, boat, or plane is direct current, because it is already available from the car, boat, or plane battery. We will now consider how high-voltage direct current is manufactured from the alternating current in the household wiring.

4-4. Direct current flows in one direction only. It leaves the negative pole of the source of supply, and returns to the source through the positive pole. This is clarified in Fig. 4-1. (You will not have to draw such a diagram for the novice examination.) Alternating current means just that: the current constantly *alternates* between a positive and a negative polarity (at a rate which has been standardized in the United States, except in a few areas, at 60 cycles per second). This simply means that a complete reversal of polarity and then back again (one cycle) occurs 60 times during each second. (See Fig. 4-2.)

---

* Permanently located station; not portable or mobile.

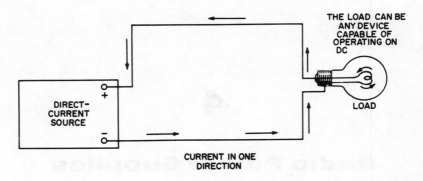

Fig. 4-1. Current flow in a DC circuit.

4-5. The direct current required for the tubes in a transmitter or receiver is not available through the house-wiring circuits. We must therefore provide some other means of producing it.

4-6. The most economical and convenient source of supply for ham radio equipment is the 115-volt alternating current available in house lighting and appliance circuits. However, this relatively low voltage would not only be ineffective (except for extremely low-powered equipment), but also *illegal*. Radio laws and regulations specify a "pure, direct current" must be used to supply the plates and screens of the transmitting tubes. Otherwise, hum would be introduced into the radio-frequency circuits. This hum would result in a much wider channel of radiation than necessary. In CW telegraphy, fewer stations would be able to operate on adjacent channels simultaneously. Such a condition could therefore be classed as "unnecessary interference," which is unlawful. In addition, the note or tone created by the use of "raw" AC, or even pulsating DC, would be not only unpleasant to the ear, but also hard to understand. For radiotelephone use, this type of current

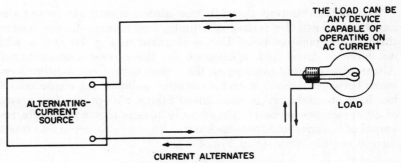

Fig. 4-2. Current flow in an AC circuit.

is *completely* out of the question. The resultant hum component in the radio-frequency carrier wave would make the speech modulation totally unintelligible. So, even though 115 volts of alternating current is most effective as a source of *primary* supply voltage, we must first change it to DC for the plate and screen supply. Tube filaments, however, can be operated directly from low-voltage alternating current because it does not affect the pure DC characteristics of the plate and screen supply.

4-7.   Tube filaments are taken care of satisfactorily by simply being supplied with alternating current from the power line. Remember, though, that a *high*-voltage alternating current must also be supplied. It is later changed to pure direct current before being applied to the plates and screens of the transmitting tubes. In Paragraph 3-17 we adopted an arbitrary 500 volts of *direct* current for the final amplifier tube plate. We explained that, through transformer action, raising the AC voltage presented no problem. Likewise, lowering the AC voltage for the filaments is simple. Paragraph 3-15 mentioned transformers in connection with the house lighting and appliance circuits, and gave you an example of how the alternating current to your home is obtained. You won't need any such monstrous cast-iron, oil-filled transformer as the one hanging on the pole near your home. However, the same principles apply. The highest-powered transformer in a novice rig weighs but a few pounds, and you can hold it in the palm of your hand! Just like his big brother on the pole, however, the little fellow has a laminated iron core, a primary winding, and one or more secondary windings. The transformer manufacturer has proportioned the number of turns between the primary and secondary so that the 115-volt input will produce the necessary voltage at the output. More turns will appear on what will become the high-voltage secondary. Perhaps the turns ratio is 1 to 5. The high voltage appearing at the secondary terminals will then be five times that impressed on the primary—or, in this case, 575 volts. Perhaps the manufacturer wants to provide 6.3 volts of AC for the filaments. He merely determines the ratio required to *reduce* the 115-volt primary value to 6.3 volts. Then he provides an additional secondary winding over the first, using the proper number of turns. Likewise, he must provide a secondary winding for the rectifier tube filament—usually 5 volts. What then? Merely a *third* secondary, properly proportioned to produce 5 volts, wound over the second one! This is shown in Fig. 4-3.

4-8.   You have now seen how the 115 volts from your house service can be both increased and decreased by a single transformer. Sometimes, particularly with higher-powered equipment than novices may use, separate transformers are employed for the filaments and plate/screen supply, rather than one with multiple secondaries. However, most transmitters in the popular ratings from 50 to 150 watts contain a single power transformer with more than one secondary winding.

4-9. Remember that the voltage at the transformer output is still *alternating*. Our job now is to change it into the pure direct current required by the plates and screens. We will need two distinct devices—a *rectifier* and a *filter*. "Rectify" (like "transform"), in its broad interpretation, means *change*. Unlike the transformer, which *changes* the alternating current to a higher or lower value,

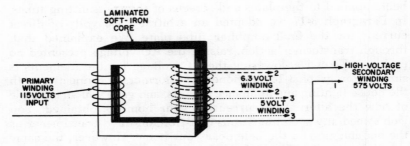

Fig. 4-3. Method of placing more than one secondary winding on a single core.

the rectifier changes the alternating current to a rough form of direct current, commonly referred to as *pulsating* DC. Although there are several types of rectifiers—such as selenium, silicon, crystal diodes, transistors, etc.—the vacuum-tube type is by far the most common. Low-powered transmitters, such as ones in the novice class, ordinarily use the high-vacuum type rectifier tube; high-powered transmitters often use a mercury vapor tube rectifier. We will consider only the high-vacuum type, however.

4-10. Alternating current, as you have already learned, reverses its direction a predetermined number of times per second. First there is a spurt of positive electricity and a rapid decay to zero, followed by a spurt of negative polarity, which also returns quickly to zero—the cycle repeating indefinitely. To fix this more firmly in your mind, examine Fig. 4-4. The rectifier, like a one-way street, permits current to flow in only one direction. This action is responsible for the pulsating form the waveshape takes after passing through the rectifier tube. The output shown to the right of the rectifier tube in Fig. 4-4A is that obtained from a *full-wave* rectifier. If the output is from a *half-wave* rectifier, the waveform appears as in Fig. 4-4B. Half-wave rectifier tubes permit only *one-half* the AC cycle to pass. On the other hand, a *full-*

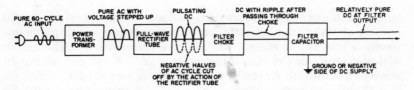

(A) Using a full-wave rectifier.

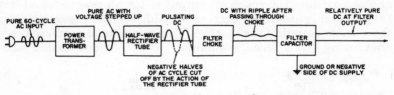

(B) Using a half-wave rectifier.

Fig. 4-4. Changing AC to DC.

wave rectifier permits *both* halves to pass alternately. Both halves, however, are passed in the same direction, because of a center-tapped secondary on the transformer, plus two half-wave tubes (mainly in high-powered transmitters), or a single tube having a filament and *two* plates. (A half-wave rectifier has only *one* plate.) Full-wave rectification is by far the more common type used in amateur transmitters. First, the output is much simpler to filter. Also, much less capacity (furnished by capacitors) and inductance (furnished by the choke) are required in the filter system. This substantially reduces the space needed, as well as the cost.

4-11. With rectification only, we still have not produced the *pure* direct current required by law. So far, all we have done is raised the voltage of the house-wiring circuits, and then changed it to a *pulsating* direct current which comes in rapid spurts—not the smooth, steady flow we need. This latter operation is a function of the *filter* section (consisting of the filter choke and capacitor). Refer to Fig. 4-5; it will clarify this for you as you read. The analogy shows two liquid filters. Obviously, an *electrical* filter cannot use a piece of screen or cloth, or a box of sand or charcoal. It does have equivalent electrical components, however, known as filter *chokes* and *capacitors*. Because it allows AC to readily pass through, but blocks any flow of DC, a capacitor is a fairly effective filter. It is connected between the positive and the negative source of DC potential. Any AC in the positive wire will pass through the capacitor and return to the negative wire, rather than go on to the transmitter tubes. A certain amount will leak through, of course. Here is where the *choke* enters the picture. A power-

47

supply choke is nothing more than half a transformer. Wound onto one leg of a rectangular soft-iron core is a single winding (as opposed to the two or more windings of a transformer). The choke will also stop—or "choke"—the passage of the AC component in the rectifier output. At the same time, it will pass the DC, although at a slightly reduced voltage because of the resistance offered by the choke coil winding. The most effective filter uses *both* a choke and a capacitor. The resultant output is, for all practical and lawful purposes, pure direct current. In addition, the choke stabilizes the voltage output of the rectifier. This is commonly referred to as "improving the voltage regulation." It is obvious that a satis-

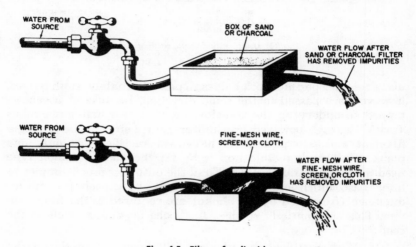

Fig. 4-5. Filters for liquids.

factory filter system for the novice transmitter power supply must consist of at least one choke and one capacitor. What may be called a "tandem" connection of additional capacitors and chokes will further purify the DC before it reaches the tubes. On the other hand, satisfactory pure direct current can be produced, with no discernible hum level in the voice circuits, by using a single capacitor and choke (of proper proportions) in the power supply. The conventional novice transmitter, whether in kit form or factory wired, usually depends upon such a single capacitor and choke combination.

4-12. Two common types of filter connections are the *capacitor input* and the *choke input*. In the capacitor input filter, the capacitor is connected directly across the output from the rectifier tube, and the choke follows it, in series with the positive lead to the transmitting tubes. The choke input filter reverses this procedure.

48

The choke coil is connected first in the positive DC lead from the rectifier, and the capacitor is connected across the positive and negative leads. The capacitor input permits a somewhat higher voltage to be used on the tube plate; on the other hand, voltage regulation is not as good as with the choke input type. A higher-voltage capacitor is usually desirable for this type of filter. The choke input filter, on the other hand, places less strain on the rectifier tube, as well as on the capacitor which follows. Although the voltage at the tube plate may be slightly less than with the capacitor input, the more desirable features of the choke input overbalance this. You will find the choke input filter used in practically all commercial amateur equipment. In summary, the power-supply filter takes the humps out of the pulsating DC from the rectifier, giving us practically pure and perfectly legal DC for the plates and screens of the transmitter tubes.

4-13. Now let's go back to Fig. 4-4. By following the waveforms produced, starting from the house-wiring circuit to the power transformer, you will see how the wave is progressively changed from a pure sine wave to a pulsating form, and eventually—after passing through the filter—to what may be considered a pure direct current, as represented by a practically straight line. Note in Fig. 4-4 that the high-voltage AC from the transformer is first rectified to rub out half of the humps. Next, the choke takes over, flattening these humps considerably. Finally, the capacitor *really* lays it on! After passing through the filter system, the AC is in effect a flat line, or a "straight line curve." Actually, if no more than four or five per cent AC ripple remains in the DC voltage after filtering, you will have a nice-sounding "note" and be perfectly legal for CW. If you are going to use radiotelephone, however, the rectifier/filter system should dispose of all but about one per cent of the AC ripple. You will find that almost all transmitters have adequate filtering to insure good voice reproduction.

4-14. All that remains to make our power supply complete is to add a bleeder resistor. Such a resistor bleeds a small amount of current across the output of the power supply. By doing so it provides better voltage regulation (less variation between minimum and maximum values), plus a discharge path for the filter capacitors after the set has been turned off. Good filter capacitors have been known to retain a charge for days unless some means is provided for discharging them. Hours after turning off a transmitter, you could inadvertently place your hand on a capacitor terminal or wiring, and receive a severe shock. Not so when a bleeder resistor is connected across the capacitor. The charge will leak off in a matter of seconds. The transformer with its primary source of power (your house-wiring circuits), the rectifier the filter system, and the bleeder resistor—all constitute a complete, legal, and entirely satisfactory power supply for the novice transmitter. A careful study of this chapter and the diagrams should enable you to answer the following questions.

4-15. *Power-Supply Questions.*

1. A rectifier, in connection with a power-supply system, serves to:

> (a) increase the AC voltage (b) change the AC to DC (c) step up the DC voltage (d) filter out the AC ripple ANSWER: (b).

It is obvious that (b) is the only possible answer. Suppose, though, that you selected (a). You have learned that AC voltage is increased by a *transformer*, not by a *rectifier*. Think what the word *rectify* means, not only in connection with power supplies, but with any subject. It merely means *change*, which immediately gives you a clue to the correct answer—to *change* AC to DC!

2. The filter in a power supply is provided to:

> (a) filter out the DC (b) change the AC to DC (c) remove the AC ripple (d) supply filament voltage to the tubes ANSWER: (c).

3. The output voltage from the rectifier is:

> (a) AC (b) pure DC (c) pulsating AC (d) pulsating DC ANSWER: (d).

4. What is the usual initial supply voltage for a radio amateur novice station?

> (a) 115 volts AC (b) 500 volts DC (c) 230 volts AC (d) 6 volts DC ANSWER: (a).

This is a question which could trip you! Note that it specifies *initial* source. *Initial* means "first." The fact that "500 volts DC" is a possible answer can mislead you if you think only in terms of what the *power supply* source in the transmitter delivers to the plates of the tubes. Just remember that you don't have that voltage *until* you have stepped up a lower voltage AC, and then rectified and filtered it! Where do you *get* the AC voltage to step up? "Through a transformer," you say. But where does the *transformer* get it? Again, your reply is prompt: "From my house-lighting circuit, through a wall plug." All right, *that* is the *initial* source of supply; and since practically all house lighting and appliance circuits have been standardized at 115 volts AC, (a) is correct.

5. Why should you turn off all voltages before working inside your transmitter?

> (a) to reduce the heating effect (b) to avoid a shock hazard (c) to reduce radiation of energy (d) to make voltage measurements ANSWER: (b).

6. A bleeder resistor in a power supply permits the voltage of the filter capacitor to:

(a) accumulate (b) leak off (c) increase (d) decrease

ANSWER: (b).

4-16. We have not touched upon safety measures, relying on your own common sense to avoid getting an electrical shock. Many persons have suffered a fatal shock from comparatively low voltages.

4-17. These are the only questions you'll be concerned with relating strictly to radio power supplies! If you have carefully studied the preceding paragraphs, you should have had no difficulty in recognizing the correct answers. Here is a good place to lay this book aside and take fifteen or twenty minutes for some code practice. Short periods of such practice provide good breaks as you study the written requirements.

5

Electrical Measurements

5-1. We can't stand on the bank alongside a dam and determine how many gallons per minute are flowing over its lip, can we? Nor can we tell, by looking at an electrical wire, how many amperes of electrical current are flowing through it. After many years of experience, we may be able to recognize the size of the wire as No. 14, for example; and our background reminds us that 15 amperes is the rated (safe) carrying capacity. But do we *know* that exactly 15 amperes are flowing through the wire? Do we *know*, just by sight, that the pressure pushing the current through the wire is 115 volts? Nature has provided us with remarkably good vision, but not that good! We require something which actually sticks its finger right into the flow of electricity and shows reaction in terms we *can* actually see! That would be a meter. A meter, in this sense, is a measuring device encased in either metal or an insulating material such as *Bakelite*. An opening (covered with glass or plastic) in the face of such a housing permits us to view a calibrated dial or scale. A pointer moves across the face of the scale. If you want a simple analogy, look at your clock. In effect, a clock is a meter (although electrical meters ordinarily have only one hand). The meter may have more than one dial or scale, all concentric, however. One scale may indicate one thing, another something else. But the one hand—or pointer, as we commonly call it—serves all scales.

5-2. A single-scale instrument of this type, with its single pointer, will indicate whatever the manufacturer has intended it for and calibrated it to—whether it be voltage (pressure), current (amperes), power (watts), etc.—and the scale will be so marked. For example, the maximum scale reading on a voltmeter may be up to 1,000 volts, or only 10 volts, or perhaps as high as 5,000 volts. If properly connected to the electrical circuit being measured, the meter can indicate, by movement of its pointer, just how many volts are present. Some meters are somewhat more intricate than others: they not only must sample the electricity being measured, but do a few internal mathematical tricks as well. You have a perfect example of this in your electric light meter. Known as a watt-hour meter, it not only determines just how many watts are being used, but also converts the wattage into watt hours. In other words, the meter indicates the total power consumed by all electrical circuits over a prescribed period of time (between meter readings). A watt-hour is just what you would guess it to be: the consumption of one watt in one hour. It is more convenient, however, to refer to watt hours in terms of kilowatt hours. Consequently, your light bill will show the number of kilowatt hours consumed in a given period, and the rate schedule will tell you the charge per kilowatt hour.

5-3. Meters are also found in your gas and water lines. Here, too, the values are indicated by pointers moving over scales or dials. As a radio amateur, whether novice or higher, you will not be particularly concerned with watt hours or their measurement. You *will*, however, stand a good chance of being asked what electrical energy is and what instrument is used to measure it. Remember, then, that the *watt* is the electrical unit of *power*, and the watt hour is the unit of electrical *energy*. Power (in watts) is measured by a wattmeter; energy, by a watt-hour meter. Make sure this distinction is clear; otherwise, it could cost you points in your examination!

5-4. Now let's consider the first, and simplest, of the electrical elements we have dealt with so far—the volt. Filament and plate or combination transformers are (except in unusual cases) supplied in the 115-volt primary sizes. When the ratio between the primary and secondary windings is properly proportioned, the correct high and low voltages will automatically appear at the secondary terminals of the transformer. The largest majority of radio tubes use 6.3 volts AC on the filament. This voltage, which is obtained from the transformer secondary, is connected directly to the filaments or heaters of the tubes. Some equipment (notably military surplus) may require a different voltage; and direct current may even have to be used for some tube filaments. Should you happen to find a good buy in surplus military gear, you can either convert the equipment to more standard voltage supplies, or provide a special supply source.

5-5. With tube filament voltages fairly standardized, there is no need for you to buy an AC voltmeter to assure that you have 6.3 volts on the filament. Take it for granted . . . a tenth of a volt one way or another won't make that much difference.

5-6. Now let's examine the high-voltage requirements of the tube plates and screens. Since you will be restricted to a power input of 75 watts to the final amplifier tube, we'll go back to our previous discussion, where we accepted 500 volts direct current as the arbitrary value your transmitter would require. This voltage will appear on the amplifier tube plate only. Just as the manufacturer makes the transformer ratios such that 6.3 volts will issue from the secondary of a transformer with a 115-volt primary, he calculates the ratio of the high-voltage winding so that it will supply a rectifier and filter system with the proper voltage to provide approximately 500 volts of pure direct current from the filter. There is no need for you to purchase a high-voltage, direct-current voltmeter to assure you of actually getting 500 volts from your power supply. That's the manufacturer's job—to supply the proper ratios in the transformer, so that the voltage will be 500 by the time it hits the plate of your final amplifier.

5-7. Since we have no particular worries about measuring the filament, plate, and screen voltages, what is left to measure? Maybe not voltage, but there is current! Even though the transformer manufacturers, as well as the makers of rectifier and filter components, can design their equipment to permit a certain current to issue from or pass through these parts, this amount represents only what you can safely use. How much of this current you actually *will* use is up to you (if you have designed and built your own transmitter) or the manufacturer. The drain, or amount of current you will use, depends upon a number of factors—chiefly the current consumption of the tubes. Obviously, if a tube with a maximum rated current of 150 milliamperes (150 *thousandths* of an ampere) is supplied from a transformer rated to deliver only *100* milliamperes safely, something is going to give. The old overload story again . . . pretty soon you may have a "cooked" transformer! On the other hand, if the transformer can handle 250 milliamperes, you are letting it coast, by drawing only 150 from it. Remember, though, that an *additional* current demand is placed upon the transformer through having to supply the plates of the oscillator and buffer/doubler tubes (if used), as well as a little current for the screen supply. These are relatively minor problems, however. If your final amplifier tube draws 150 milliamperes and the transformer has a normal rated capacity of 250 milliamperes, you need not worry—your transformer can handle the entire job without overload.

5-8. As long as the manufacturer has designed the transformer to produce 500 to 600 volts, his only problem is to insulate the windings enough to withstand this potential. A reliable manufacturer will generally provide a 200 or 300 per cent safety factor, since the additional cost is relatively small. Although he can design the transformer to permit a *current* drain of up to 250 milliamperes (or whatever other figure the design calls for), he cannot be a mind reader and know how much of this available current your transmitter is going to use. He does know that you can't use any more voltage than his design has provided. Moreover, he knows you'll probably use it all. To get *more*, you'd either have to use a larger transformer (voltagewise), or do a lot of trick circuitry in the rectifier system.

5-9. So, the *current* consumed by your transmitting tubes is something you'll have to determine for yourself. The tubes have a *normal* rated current which you should not exceed. Exceeding it by as much as 100% (or even more) is so easy, however, when you are tuning a transmitter, that you could ruin a tube (and maybe your transformer, rectifier, and filter system) within just a few seconds if you didn't know the current drain. Here, then, is where we do need a "watchdog"—a meter to measure current. Fortunately, the demand—and consequent high production—has made it possible for manufacturers to price such meters very nominally; and no intelligent manufacturer of amateur transmitters, nor the ham who builds his own, would think for a minute of leaving such a meter out of the rig.

5-10. Because the novice transmitter can never legally use currents as high as one ampere on the tubes, it follows that a meter with a scale which reads only in amperes would be rather difficult to use for accurately determining the current flow. Hence, current meters in amateur transmitters are calibrated in milliamperes, with various full-scale readings. A typical milliammeter is shown in Fig. 5-1. For the novice transmitter using a maximum of 150 milliamperes, a full-scale reading of 250 milliamps will provide a good safety factor if the novice does his tuning intelligently, and

Fig. 5-1. A meter calibrated in milliamperes.

yet give him better than a half-scale reading at the point of resonance. On the other hand, a higher scale reading—up to one amp—will give him a good safety factor when he goes to higher power.

5-11. Up to now, we've referred primarily to the voltage and current on the plate of the final amplifier tube. What about the oscillator and perhaps the buffer/doubler tube? Don't we have the same problem there? Yes and no! It would be handy if we could afford meters *everywhere* voltage and current are found in a transmitter. Handy, but pretty nonessential! We have other means of handling this problem, from both a more sensible—and certainly a more economical—standpoint. Let's look at the oscillator tube. Although its voltage may be in the neighborhood of 250 volts, its current requirements are minor. The crystal-type oscillator, which is mandatory for a novice, usually requires twenty to thirty milliamperes (let's call them "mils" from now on, as the more experienced ham does). We'll go a little further, although a more complete explanation won't appear until the next chapter. Your oscillator simply will not oscillate unless its resonant circuit is tuned to the proper frequency. If it does not oscillate, the transmitter will not work (unless it goes into illegal self-oscillation in the final, which you'll learn about later). If it *does* oscillate properly, it will be close to resonance, which means it is drawing just about the minimum current required. So, why worry about "how much," to the extent of providing a meter? This also applies to the buffer/doubler stage; the transmitter is not going to be effective unless this intermediate stage is tuned closely to resonance with the oscillator, or to a harmonic frequency. How are you going to know? There's a term we're going to come across later, known as *grid drive*. Briefly, this is merely the power required from the oscillator to excite (drive) the next stage (be it a buffer/doubler or the final amplifier) efficiently. Likewise, a buffer/doubler stage, if used, must supply the final amplifier with enough drive to be effective. Handbooks, construction manuals, tube data books, kit instructions, and numerous other sources specify how much grid current in mils is required to drive a particular tube. Your only problem is to determine whether you are getting sufficient mils to accomplish this—which a meter will tell you. You can connect a second milliammeter in the grid circuit of the final amplifier (or in the grid of every tube, if you are really a stickler for watching the needles flick!). But you don't *need* to. Practically all manufacturers of complete transmitters, as well as those in kit form, provide a milliammeter. It will have two scales and one pointer, although some have only one scale and pointer. It really makes no difference. What *is* important is that they have a switch which places into the circuit certain resistance values (review "resistance" in Chapter 3, if necessary) when the switch is in one position and different values in other positions. This allows you to read the grid-circuit current of the final amplifier in the one position and the plate-circuit current in the other. What more do you need? A properly designed transmitter, intelligently tuned and operated, will have adequate metering. When the voltages and currents specified for the allowable watts input are used, its operation—from the power-input standpoint—will be perfectly legal and efficient.

5-12. Although the metering requirements for your transmitter proper have been taken care of, you may be wondering how you can determine the resistance of a circuit. In other words, how can you find a short circuit, other than by the smoke-and-fire method? It's a good question; let's explore it.

5-13. The resistance of a component is measured by an *ohmmeter*, which also has the familiar scale and pointer. With this meter, you can read resistance directly from the scale, even up into the *millions* of ohms! Unlike the milliammeter, which is almost always built into a radio transmitter or receiver, an ohmmeter is so versatile that it serves a much better purpose as a portable instrument, useful on the bench or in the field. All radio and TV service shops have such a meter; they would be sunk without one. You see, although the currents in a radio transmitter are subject to many variables (depending upon tuning and adjustment as well as possible malfunctioning), the voltages, too, sometimes are so affected. Resistance values are practically always fixed, and such fixed resistances cannot be changed by external adjustments. When they *do* shift, you have trouble on your hands, which means you will have to tear the transmitter down to find it! Hence, not much point in combining an ohmmeter in the transmitter itself, when such a versatile device can be used for so many jobs—even for testing your toaster, percolator, and other household appliances!

5-14. A considerable number of manufacturers make such ohmmeters. The meters are housed in compact, substantial cases of metal or insulating material. They are equipped with flexible test leads, which you can use as "feelers" on a suspected piece of equipment. Most manufacturers have carried their design quite a bit further. These most versatile meters measure not only resistance, but also—by an ingenious arrangement of switches, plugs, and multi-scales over which a single pointer moves—voltage, both AC and DC, high and low; and current in milliamperes, over an amazingly wide range. A meter of this type is shown in Fig. 5-2. Known in the trade as *volt-ohm-milliammeters* (VOM's), they are surprisingly low in cost. Some, offered in kit form which you assemble yourself, are even under twenty dollars!

5-15. And now, before going any further, we're going to slip another little formula in front of you—Ohm's law. Actually, Ohm's law is almost as simple as the formula we gave you in Chapter 3 for determining power ("voltage multiplied by amperes represents power in watts"). Ohm's law is merely a simple equation wherein, if two of the electrical elements are known, the third can readily be found. The three elements we are concerned with are

Fig. 5-2. The Heathkit Model MM1 volt-ohm-milliammeter.

volts (pressure), amperes (current), and ohms (resistance). In Ohm's law we use the letters E to designate voltage (electromotive force), I for current, and R for resistance. Let's assume we know the voltage (E) and resistance (R). The current (I) is the unknown. Here's the first equation:

$$I = \frac{E}{R}$$

5-16. For simplicity, let's give E a value of 100, and R a value of 10. Now substitute 100 for E and 10 for R. When we divide 100 by 10, we get 10, the value of I. We now know that a circuit which has 100 volts (E) pushing current (I) through a resistance (R) of 10 ohms will have a current value of 10 amperes. It's that easy!

5-17. Now let's turn the tables a bit. We'll use the same figures, 10 and 100. This time, however, suppose we know that the voltage is 100 and the current is 10. What is the resistance? You'll have to change your fraction around. *Resistance* is now the unknown element, represented by R. The formula then becomes:

$$R = \frac{E}{I}$$

Substitute the numerical values and we have:

$$R = \frac{100}{10}$$

Dividing E by I gives us 10. Therefore, the resistance is 10 ohms.

5-18. By knowing the current and the resistance, we can also determine the voltage just as simply. This time, the formula becomes E $=$ IR, which means that I multiplied by R (current times resistance) equals the voltage. Putting our numerals back in place, we have something like this:

$$E = 10 \times 10$$

Ten times ten is one hundred, the amount of voltage.

5-19. Ohm's law is purely a case of memorizing the arrangement of the symbols. Should you be asked, "What is Ohm's law?" you need only show it as follows:

$$R = \frac{E}{I} \qquad\qquad I = \frac{E}{R} \qquad\qquad E = IR$$

As an aid in remembering this formula, examine Fig. 5-3. Think of it as E, I, and R placed on a coin, as shown in Fig. 5-3A. To find the correct formula, place your thumb over the unknown value. For example, to find E, the voltage, place your thumb over E, as shown in Fig. 5-3B. The formula for finding E becomes obvious (I $\times$ R $=$E). Likewise, to find I, place your thumb over I (Fig. 5-3C). Now you see the formula, E over R (E $\div$ R). The same holds true for finding the value of R in Fig. 5-3D—E $\div$ I $=$ R.

5-20. Now let's run through a few questions on electrical measurements.

1. What device is used to measure electrical energy?

    (a) wattmeter (b) ammeter (c) watt-hour meter (d) voltmeter
    ANSWER: (c).

2. Electrical pressure is measured by what instrument?

    (a) voltmeter (b) wavemeter (c) ohmmeter (d) ammeter
    ANSWER: (a).

3. A wattmeter measures:

    (a) energy (b) pressure (c) current (d) power ANSWER: (d).

Is your head swimming after trying to decide between *wattmeter*

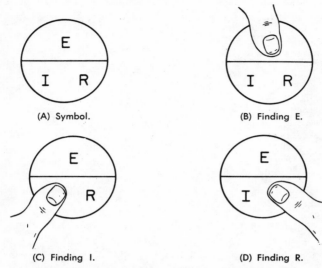

(A) Symbol.

(B) Finding E.

(C) Finding I.

(D) Finding R.

Fig. 5-3. A method of remembering the formula for Ohm's law.

and *watt-hour* meter? It just takes concentration; read back and then figure it out!

4. Resistance is determined by means of a:
    (a) voltmeter (b) joulemeter (c) ammeter (d) ohmmeter
                                         ANSWER: (d).

5. In Ohm's law, which of the following is incorrect?
    (a) $E = IR$ (b) $R = \dfrac{E}{I}$ (c) $R = EI$ (d) $I = \dfrac{E}{R}$
                                         ANSWER: (c).

6. With 10 amperes flowing at a pressure of 100 volts, the resistance of the circuit would be:
    (a) 20 ohms (b) 10 ohms (c) 100 ohms (d) 5 ohms
                                         ANSWER: (b).

7. What instrument measures electrical current?
    (a) voltmeter (b) ammeter (c) wattmeter (d) ohmmeter
                                         ANSWER: (b).

All of the foregoing questions depend more or less upon memorization. Your study of Chapter 3, "Basic Electricity," should have given you a well-rounded picture of what you need to know for this chapter. If you missed a few points in the first reading, reread Chapter 3.

6

The Radio Transmitter

6-1. With the discussion of radio transmission, we enter into consideration of *radio* circuits, rather than the more purely *electrical* ones discussed in previous chapters. The heart of all radio transmission and reception is the vacuum electron tube (and more recently, the transistor). Vacuum tubes, which are of various shapes and sizes (Fig. 6-1), contain two or more elements within a glass or metallic enclosure. The enclosure, known as the envelope, is exhausted to a high vacuum. Some of the more recent amateur tubes are even enclosed in ceramic envelopes. All tubes are equipped with a base from which extend pins or prongs of metal. The pins permit external connection, through a suitable socket, to the elements within the tube envelope.

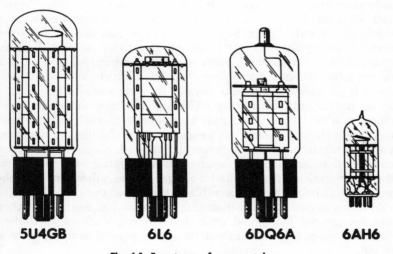

5U4GB   6L6   6DQ6A   6AH6

Fig. 6-1. Four types of vacuum tubes.

6-2. The electron tube is basically a valve: it passes electrons between the elements and through the enclosed space in the envelope. In fact, it is still referred to in England as a valve. The history of the vacuum tube, which had its humble beginning from Thomas Edison's carbon-filament electric lamp, would fill many volumes. We recommend that you study various publications which give a more comprehensive treatment of the theory and application of electron tubes. You will find such study to be invaluable, not only in your daily amateur operation, but also in preparing you for the higher-class license exams. We are going to discuss only the bare essentials which will enable you to pass the examination for your novice license.

6-3. We have briefly referred to oscillators, buffer/doublers, and final amplifiers in earlier chapters. These are the vacuum electron tubes you will meet in your novice transmitter. The oscillator tube is a *must* in *any* radio transmitter. The buffer/doubler tube and the final amplifier tube are not needed to radiate a signal into space . . . the oscillator alone can do that! So, let's examine oscillator tubes and their related circuits. We'll first consider just what oscillation means, radiowise, and what is responsible for it. When you study the requirements for the novice class license, you will find that a novice transmitter in the amateur class must be *crystal* controlled. Without a knowledge of radio principles, such a statement will be completely foreign to you.

6-4. The word *crystal*, with reference to radio transmitters, refers to a small piece of quartz, usually rectangular or square, approximately one square inch in size. The surfaces of the "rock" (as most amateurs call it) may be ground, for example, to a thickness of only $\frac{1}{32}$ inch. Do not confuse this crystal with the rectifier in crystal detector receiving sets prior to 1920. Various minerals were used then, such as carborundum, silicon, galena, or cerusite. All had *rectifying* properties which made radio reception possible. The quartz crystal in your transmitter is used in an entirely different sense. Although we mention *quartz* specifically, other types of crystals also possess piezoelectric properties. *Piezoelectric* means the property of producing an electrical voltage when mechanical stress is applied. Conversely, when connected to an electrical source, these crystals will vibrate at the frequency of the applied voltage. These vibrations will be vigorous, although not discernible to the naked eye. Much weaker vibrations occur at other than this resonant frequency, but they can be ignored in a good crystal. This frequency of oscillation depends upon (1) the dimensions of the crystal and (2) how it is cut.

6-5. Since quartz crystals are used most extensively in oscillators, we will consider only them. You'll probably never encounter the others—not in amateur practice at least. A perfect crystal has a hexagonal cross section, as shown in Fig. 6-2A. Thin sheets are cut from the natural crystal and then ground to the thickness needed for the desired resonant frequency at which they are to vibrate. The thinner the crystal, the higher the frequency. The 80-meter crystals, which will operate in the novice 3700-3750 kilocycle band, will be approximately twice as thick as those in the 7150-7200 kilocycle band.

(A) Shape of crystal in its natural form.

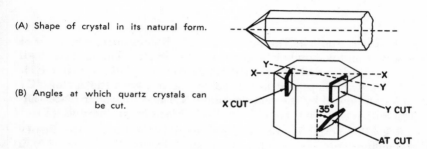

(B) Angles at which quartz crystals can be cut.

Fig. 6-2. The quartz crystal.

6-6. The *cut* of the crystal refers to the way the final quartz plate is cut from the natural mineral. All crystals are cut at various angles (Fig. 6-2B), designated as X, Y, AT, BT, CT, DT, and GT. You will encounter only the X and Y and maybe the AT cuts. The others are special cuts which, for precision laboratory and commercial use, require a lower coefficient of temperature drift (the change in the resonant frequency of the crystal as the temperature changes). Only in exceptional cases does an amateur use them; we doubt if you ever will. You'll not encounter any questions on this subject in your novice examination.

6-7. This, then, gives you some idea of what the crystal or rock is that is mentioned so frequently in amateur literature. To anyone with the least smattering of mechanical knowledge, it is obvious that such a quartz plate cannot be connected into a circuit by merely soldering wires to the two surfaces. You don't solder to a rock! Light, but firm, electrical contact with the two plane surfaces of the crystal is a must, though. This is achieved through a small device known as a crystal holder (Fig. 6-3). Ordinarily, your crystal comes factory-sealed in such a holder. Two prongs (like the ones on vacuum tubes) permit the crystal to be plugged into a suitable socket. A disassembled crystal holder

Fig. 6-3. A typical crystal holder.

is shown in Fig. 6-4. The holder is a small enclosure, generally of *Bakelite* and somewhat larger than the crystal. The crystal itself (A) is sandwiched between the two contact plates (B and B1). The sandwich is placed in the holder cavity, with the spring (C) on top, followed by the retainer plate (D) and the cover plate (E). The entire assembly is held rigidly in place by the screws (F).

6-8. We could go on and on, explaining the entire theory connected with an oscillating crystal circuit. However, if you turn out to be a typical ham, you'll discard your crystal anyway, in favor of the variable frequency oscillator, the minute you re-

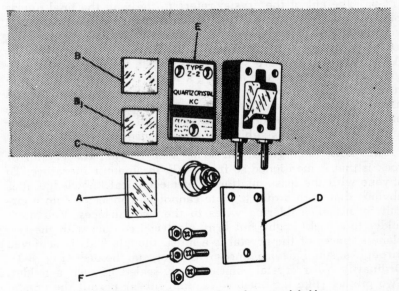

Fig. 6-4. The internal construction of a crystal holder.

ceive your general class license. A crystal-controlled oscillator does have a definite limitation—you would need a separate crystal and holder for every frequency you wanted to use. At approximately three dollars each for good crystals in holders, you could buy a new automobile for the cost of enough crystals to cover all of the frequencies an amateur can legally use! Nevertheless, the federal law states that you must have a crystal-controlled transmitter while you are operating on a novice class license. Your apprentice period limits you to a few rather narrow frequency bands, and there are only a few areas in each band where you will find a relatively clear spot to transmit. So, why buy a barrelful of crystals when you can use only a few? The average novice is generally supplied with about three crystals. If you intend to be a VFO-equipped station after you become a general class ham, you'll cast your crystals aside anyway. They will all be in the novice or apprentice bands; you will have become a journeyman, with many more privileges and a much wider choice of frequencies.

6-9. Let's say your first crystal will be one which will oscillate, or vibrate, at a frequency of 3735 kilocycles. This pretty much guarantees that your radiation will be legal, since the 80-meter, or 3500-kilocycle, band for novices extends from 3700 to 3750 kilocycles. Therefore, a crystal with a frequency of 3735 *kilocycles* will vibrate three million, seven-hundred and thirty-five thousand cycles per second. Simplicity of expression was the incentive for reducing cycles to kilocycles. Progress dictated a change, first from wavelength to frequency; then, with increasing frequency, awkward numerical expressions were reduced to ones more readily handled. A further simplification appeared, to keep pace with the higher and higher frequencies. The term *megacycle* entered the picture. *Mega* means million. Therefore, a megacycle equals one million cycles (or 1000 kilocycles). A crystal frequency of 3735 *kilo*cycles then becomes 3.735 megacycles. The term *megacycles* is used to express the frequency bands to which amateurs are entitled. For example, the 3500- to 4000-kilocycle band is commonly referred to as the 3.5- to 4.0-megacycle band. (Quite a few amateurs still refer to this band as the 80-meter band for the low end and the 75-meter band for the high end. This is a loose phraseology, a carryover from earlier days when wavelength rather than frequency was used.) You will express frequency in either kilocycles or megacycles (although you, too, may occasionally use the term *meter* as you become a more experienced ham).

6-10. Now let's talk about the oscillator circuit, but without a long discourse on how it operates. The emission of electrons from the hot filament or heater in the tube, and the application of a voltage to the plate, permits a current to flow through a resonant plate circuit (one tuned to the frequency of your crystal). Some energy is fed back to the grid, and the circuit starts oscillating (meaning simply that the current flow changes direction, the same as in the alternating current discussed in connection with power supplies in Chapter 3), at the frequency for which the crystal has been ground. Remember that vibration of the crystal also sets up a mechanical stress. As we have learned, a crystal subjected to such stress will generate a voltage. Suffice it to say that the combination of components, circuitry, and applied voltage and current in the oscillator circuit sets up radio-frequency oscillations. If you hold a small neon bulb close to the tank coil of the oscillator (about an inch or so), it will glow without actually touching the wire of the coil. Likewise, when a small pickup loop is soldered to a flashlight bulb, the bulb will glow brightly when brought near the oscillator coil. This is illustrated in Fig. 6-5.

CAUTION: Even though the voltage in the oscillator tank coil is relatively low, *do not* touch the coil, because you can get a nasty shock, to say the least. Hold the bulb by its glass envelope while you are bringing the pickup loop or neon-bulb base close to the coil.

6-11. What phenomenon is causing the bulb to light, even though it is not connected to any source of power? This is *radio-frequency radiation;* it is exactly what happens when a transmitter is connected to an antenna system. The radiation goes from the antenna wire into free space. Unlike the radiation from the

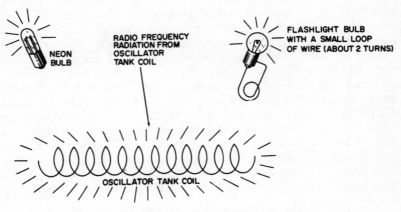

Fig. 6-5. A simple test to determine if oscillator stage is working.

oscillator tank coil, which is limited to an inch or so from the coil, the radiation from the antenna travels through the air for hundreds, and even thousands, of miles in all directions. A similar antenna at a distant station detects this minute current and makes it audible in a sensitive receiver. Through the receiver circuitry and amplifier tubes, this current appears as the original signal which was transmitted hundreds of miles away.

6-12. Let's consider just why this radio-frequency phenomenon permits us to light lamps without wires and to radiate an intelligible signal through free space. We mentioned earlier that the standard line voltage to the home is 115 volts at a frequency of 60 cycles per second. This is the power-line frequency; it simply means the AC current is changing direction sixty times each second. This may seem rather fast; however, it is considered a very low frequency. In radio circuits, the frequencies run up into the millions of cycles per second. In fact, the AC current frequency *must* be *high* before it will radiate properly for communications purposes. It is the radiation from this high-frequency current that causes the lamp to glow. The low frequencies in homes and industry stay pretty well confined to the wires in which they flow.

6-13. Much more enters into the theory and practical application of radio-frequency phenomena, but we've already given you more than you will need for your novice examination. All you have to know is that it is a phenomenon peculiar to high-frequency alternating current. It's what makes radio communication possible.

6-14. We've casually referred to buffer/doublers in previous pages, with no thought of going into an explanation until we reached this chapter. Now that we're here, let's be more explicit. The simple oscillator transmitter just described is a satisfactory transmitter for the novice amateur, within its power limitations. It *is* restricted in that sense, however. Ordinarily, the oscillator in a radio transmitter is a "flea-powered" gadget. Anywhere from five to fifteen watts is about right for the run-of-the-mill oscillator. Without too much strain on the equipment components, tube, and crystal, an oscillator can withstand about double that power input. In fact, successful oscillator transmitters with as much as fifty watts input power have been operated. A number have proven entirely satisfactory with as much as 75 watts applied power, the novice amateur's legal limit. Just the same, the more experienced amateur thinks twice before he asks the poor oscillator to handle a 50-watt power input; at the mere thought of a 75-watt input, he is apt to shy away. At those higher powers, it is not at all difficult to shatter a crystal or ruin a tube! Carefully handled, the oscillator will take it. The thinking along these lines, however, is to pursue a less touchy approach to the problem. In a radio receiver, the very weak signals picked up by the antenna are amplified before they are reproduced as sound. In a transmitter, the procedure is followed in reverse. The relatively weak output from a low-powered oscillator is amplified before reaching the antenna.

6-15. We merely need to amplify the output of our oscillator through the use of an additional tube. However, amateurs (excepting the novice class) are allowed a power *input* up to one kilowatt—1,000 watts! Suppose the oscillator is running at about 15 watts input, and—assuming 50% efficiency—is delivering 7.5 watts of radio-frequency current. We want a final amplifier tube which will permit us to apply enough voltage and current to its plate to equal (by multiplying the two values, remember?) the maximum 1,000 watts, or 1 kilowatt, which the higher-class amateur licensees are permitted. That's asking a lot, isn't it? One tube, putting out less than ten watts, must drive a second tube to produce more than 100 times as much!

6-16. It *can* be done, however. Development of vacuum tubes with increasing efficiency makes such a design possible. Again, though, you're clubbing the mule to death to make him move! As long as we know that a vacuum electron tube will amplify once, there is no reason why a second stage cannot be used to further amplify, and a third stage, and so on. Hence, intermediate stages were developed. These took the output of the oscillator and built it up to a reasonable amount. This output was then fed into another tube which further amplified it until, in two or three easy stages, the power reaching the antenna had been increased to the desired amount. Although such tubes acted as amplifiers, they also had several other desirable properties. Because it followed the oscillator stage, the amplifier served as a buffer between the oscillator circuit and the antenna. As such, it helped stabilize the oscillator frequency through such isolation. Soon they became known as *buffer amplifiers*. Then it was discovered that if the amplifier circuits were tuned to a multiple of the oscillator frequency, an output of two or three (or even more) times the initial frequency could be obtained. These are known as harmonic frequencies, and the amplifier stage was termed buffer/doubler (or tripler, quadrupler, etc.). The correct technical term for these stages is *frequency multipliers*, for which purpose they are primarily used. The buffering effect remains; but their amplification is relatively small, and becomes even less when higher multiples of the oscillator frequency are amplified. Therefore, higher-powered transmitters also include straight intermediate-amplifier stages. Their sole purpose is to build up the signal enough to excite, or drive, the final amplifier tube, often referred to as a power amplifier. You, as a novice, probably will not be too concerned with the subject of frequency multiplication in the operation of your own transmitting equipment. You will, however, find a few elementary questions on that subject in your examination, along with an occasional mention of doubling and tripling. Therefore, we have attempted to give you sufficient information to see you through. Now, let's get along to the final amplifier tube, the one which feeds the amplified energy into the antenna circuits for radiation to someone's receiver.

6-17. We have just completed a little discussion on intermediate amplifiers. The word *intermediate* should immediately suggest to you just what it is—something in between. You have probably figured out that an intermediate amplifier, which we have referred to as a buffer amplifier and as a buffer doubler, most certainly cannot be the last word—something must follow it. It depends! If the intermediate amplifier is the only tube following the oscillator, it is no longer intermediate—it is the *final* tube. Moreover, we might go so far as to say that if the oscillator tube is the *only* tube in the transmitter, *it* can then be considered as the final, as well as the initial, tube.

6-18. As we previously pointed out, it is entirely possible and practical to build a crystal-controlled oscillator containing just one tube with a power input of 75 watts, the maximum permitted the radio amateur novice. Such an oscillator will provide sufficient power to permit communication over many hundreds, and even thousands, of miles. As we also explained, it would take a pretty fair understanding of radio principles to properly adjust such a transmitter for maximum efficiency without shattering the crystal, and maybe ruining the tube and causing other damage here and there. If we limit the power input to 50 watts, we're treating the crystal, tube, and other components a bit more gently. However, we are still on the precarious side. Let's get the power input down to a point where we feel we have our oscillator pretty well under control. You'll have a very effective crystal oscillator/transmitter if the input is somewhere around 25 watts. Furthermore, nothing in the set will suffer.

6-19. So far, we have considered the oscillator as a transmitter. Used in this manner, it doubles as both the oscillator and the final amplifier; in fact, it is the *only* radio tube in the rig. The average novice, however, is inclined to look longingly at the 75 watts maximum which he is permitted. How to get it safely and inexpensively—here is where "Mr. Final Amplifier" enters the picture. It is only necessary to feed the output of the oscillator stage into a larger tube, running at higher voltage and equivalent current, to make up an input power of 75 watts. The final tube then feeds the antenna circuits, and the signals go flying off into space. The final amplifier is no different from the straight intermediate amplifier previously described, except in the size of the tube, the circuit components, and the applied power.

6-20. If we are going to use a two-tube or two-stage transmitter running at 75 watts input, we most certainly don't need all the wallop a 25-watt oscillator generates. The answer is obvious: we can use a much smaller oscillator, with only a few watts input, and with a smaller tube and other circuit components. What we save will buy the final amplifier tube, and maybe a few odds and ends. The small tubes used in driver oscillators of this type ordinarily operate with a plate voltage of somewhere between 150 and 250 volts, and a current of about 15 to 30 milliamperes. (Voltages and currents vary widely, depending upon the choice of tubes, but these are about average.) The output from even the smallest crystal oscillator is more than enough to drive the grid of a modern final amplifier tube to full efficiency. Means are frequently provided to reduce the driving power to avoid damaging the final amplifier tube.

6-21. With the 500-volt power supply in our hypothetical transmitter, it is simple to obtain the 150-250 volts for the oscillator plate. All we have to do is adjust the slider on the voltage-divider resistance described earlier. However, the full 500 volts would be applied to the plate of the final tube. If the final tube is the screen-grid type, the 150 volts or so required for the screen are also obtained from the voltage divider. This is done by adjusting an additional slider, or by proper proportioning of resistors if more than one is used. With 500 volts on the plate of the final, what will we need to make up a power input of 75 watts? Go back to your formula for power: $W = EI$. Current is the unknown in our problem. Therefore, our formula becomes watts divided by volts equals current $(I = W \div E)$. Dividing 75 watts by 500 volts will give 0.15 ampere (150 milliamperes) as the required current. Hence, our final amplifier tube will draw 150 milliamperes. At 500 volts, this is the maximum 75 watts you are allowed.

6-22. You now have an economical, crystal-controlled transmitter which will enable you to operate legally. When connected to a suitable antenna, it will let you communicate with other amateurs over many thousands of miles. The antenna need be nothing more than a single copper wire of random length, or it may be an elaborate arrangement of rotating elements known as a beam. There are as many variations between these extremes as there are amateurs! You will not be called upon to answer questions on antennas in your novice examination.

6-23. We do want to emphasize one more point—the distinction between radio*telegraph* and radio*telephone*. The various types of emissions—such as radiotelegraph and radiotelephone, to name just a few—are given prefix designations. A complete list of these can be found in Appendix C. However, you will be concerned with only a few of them in your novice exam. For example, CW (telegraphy) is designated A-1 emission; tone-modulated CW, A-2; and AM (amplitude-modulated) radiotelephone, A-3. All of your novice work will be with radiotelegraphy (CW).

6-24. While operating as a CW amateur, you may discover that you have bad key clicks. That is, minute sparking takes place as you open and close the key contacts. Frequently this sparking flows back into your transmitter circuits as weak radiation. If it gets through your final circuits and into your antenna, an annoying click will be produced each time you make or break the key contacts. These are spurious (meaning false) and unwanted radiations; they seriously interfere with other radio operation, and are definitely illegal. They are suppressed by means of a small capacitor and, if required, one or two small RF choke coils. Such a combination is known as a key click filter; it acts much like a power-supply filter in smoothing out and eliminating these abrupt surges. Keep this in mind, and make sure *your* transmitter is not guilty. Ask a neighboring ham to listen and report any evidence of clicks. Also be prepared to answer a question or two about the key click filter in your examination.

6-25. You will be asked a few questions on radiotelephone, so we'd best consider a few more points. Radiotelephone modulation is a method whereby the electrical equivalent of sound (an audio signal) is impressed (superimposed) upon a radio-frequency carrier. (The voice rides on the carrier.) There are other forms of modulation (such as tone); but we will not burden you with them, since they do not appear in your novice examination.

6-26. Modulation, too, has its "key clicks," although they are not spoken of as such. The common term for spurious radiations from radiophone transmitters is *overmodulation*, which generates unwanted sidebands. Whereas the keyed carrier in CW operation is confined to extremely narrow channels, that of the radiophone requires a considerably broader path to accommodate the modulated signals. Recent development has narrowed this path considerably, but it is still somewhat wider than a CW signal. A properly adjusted phone transmitter will remain strictly within the confines of its radiation channel. Improper design or adjustment will cause it to wander outside its channel on both sides, creating what are known as spurious sidebands. These sidebands are not actually required for transmitting intelligence by radiophone. In ham parlance, they are often referred to as *splatter*, which causes serious interference with signals on adjacent channels. Splatter can (and frequently does) interfere with radio broadcast reception, and may even extend to other channels outside the amateur bands. Regardless of its effect, such radiation is distinctly illegal, and will bring a citation (or more serious consequences) if allowed to continue. The maximum modulation percentage permitted an amateur radiophone station is 100 per cent, which represents full use of the *legal* channel width. When the modulation percentage *exceeds* 100 per cent, you are overmodulating. This will cause spurious sidebands. Better to maintain your modulation level below 100 per cent; 85 to 95 per cent will provide adequate modulation and still allow you to transmit perfectly intelligible speech.

6-27.   Before going into a question-and-answer session on this chapter, we want to mention a different type of interference creator which can also cause you considerable trouble. This is parasitic oscillation. These "bad actors" are radio-frequency oscillations occurring in your transmitter at random frequencies, often far removed from the crystal frequency. They might be anywhere in or out of an amateur band! These are the types of oscillations your key clicks create, for example. The crystal frequency, although perfectly legal, does not ensure against these parasitics; they can often be blamed on other causes than keying, such as poor design or maladjustment of the circuits. The idea here is to prevent them by using the proper key click filter where required, as well as standard proven design techniques, reliable parts, and shielding of any parts that could be possible offenders.

6-28.   Well, that was quite a session, wasn't it? Now let's "radiate" a handful of questions at you to see what you've gained from it. And don't call these questions "spurious radiations," for you're going to have to answer your share of them in the examination!

1. A radio-frequency oscillator is:

    (a) a generator of radio-frequency oscillations   (b) a radio tube
    (c) a quartz crystal   (d) a vibrating reed   ANSWER: (a).

Obviously, a tube alone won't oscillate; neither will a quartz crystal. Therefore, (a) is the only correct answer.

2. A frequency multiplier:

(a) determines the frequency of the oscillator   (b) causes oscillation
(c) increases the frequency in multiples of the fundamental   (d) rectifies
ANSWER: (c).

That, too, is pretty obvious; your clue is in the word *multiplies*, if you haven't learned the answer well enough otherwise!

3. What is the maximum power input in watts permitted for the operation of an amateur radio novice station?

(a) 100   (b) 10   (c) 75   (d) 1000   ANSWER (c).

4. What method of frequency control must be used in a novice transmitter?

(a) master oscillator   (b) crystal   (c) frequency multiplier   (d) variable frequency oscillator   ANSWER: (b).

5. What is the accepted abbreviation for unmodulated radio-telegraph emission?

(a) VFO   (b) ICW   (c) CW   (d) GMT   ANSWER: (c).

Remember, earlier—CW means *continuous-wave telegraphy.*

6. Modulation is the process by which:

(a) the audio frequency is superimposed on a radio-frequency carrier
(b) unwanted sidebands are eliminated   (c) audio tones are created
(d) audible sounds are removed from a carrier   ANSWER: (a).

Look up *superimposed* in your dictionary, if you're not sure of its meaning.

7. A kilocycle is:

(a) 100 cycles   (b) 1000 cycles   (c) 10 cycles   (d) 1,000,000 cycles
ANSWER: (b).

That's a memory answer, but you'd better know it!

8. Which of the following represents megacycles?

(a) kc   (b) meters   (c) mc   (d) mfd   ANSWER: (c).

Bet you didn't catch this in the text, but that's it. This is another memory answer. Study the Glossary in the back of this book for a number of common radio abbreviations.

9. Current in the plate circuit of an amateur radio transmitter is measured in:

(a) volts   (b) watts   (c) kilocycles   (d) milliamperes
ANSWER: (d).

10. A key click filter is used to:

(a) suppress unwanted spurious radiations   (b) keep the key from sticking   (c) prevent shock to the operator   (d) make keying easier
ANSWER: (a).

If you missed this question, go back and read the text again!

11. What power is applied to the plate of a tube if the voltage is 650 volts and the current is 90 milliamperes?

    (a) 75 watts   (b) 50 watts   (c) 58.5 watts   (d) 90 watts

ANSWER: (c).

Power is expressed in watts; volts times amperes equals watts. But you're dealing in 90 *milli*amperes, or .09 amperes; .09 times 650 is 58.5 watts.

12. What is the third harmonic of 3750 kilocycles?

    (a) 7500 kc   (b) 1875 kc   (c) 11,250 kc   (d) 1250 kc ANSWER: (c).

Careful here, also. We barely touched upon the word *harmonic* in our discussion of frequency multipliers, but it's there. In a nutshell, the *second* harmonic is *twice* the fundamental frequency; the *third* harmonic, *three* times, and so on.

13. Generation of spurious sidebands in radiotelephone operation is a result of:

    (a) overmodulation   (b) undermodulation   (c) key clicks   (d) hum

ANSWER: (a).

14. In a frequency multiplier designed to double, would you expect the output frequency to be:

    (a) cut in half   (b) tripled   (c) twice the fundamental   (d) three times the fundamental   ANSWER: (c).

Think! (a) is out because you can't cut something in half by multiplying! (b) would be tripling, and so would (d). (c) is, of course, merely another way of saying *doubled*.

15. The power input to the final amplifier tube is determined by:

    (a) dividing voltage by resistance   (b) multiplying volts by amperes
    (c) Ohm's law   (d) voltmeter   ANSWER: (b).

Even though you will use values of less than one ampere, expressed in decimals, the answer will *still* be based upon volts times amps, although expressed for convenience as *milli*amperes.

6-29. If you find you're a bit hazy at points, go back and review the whole chapter. Do it more than once, if necessary; be *sure* you've absorbed all the information in this chapter before going on to the next. It's time you took a break anyway; so, set up your code-practice gear and give the code a good workout.

7

Legal Aspects of Transmitter Adjustment and Operation

7-1. By now you have probably acquired a communications receiver and have just about decided on your initial transmitter. Whether your choice is a simple five-watt crystal oscillator, or something capable of delivering the full 75-watt maximum, your transmitter will radiate! In fact, it will radiate even *without an antenna*. Not far perhaps—a fraction of a mile with five-watts input, or several miles if you are using greater power.

7-2. Federal radio laws define illegal operation as ". . . radiation of radio frequency signals into free space without a proper, valid federal license if such radiations are *capable* of interfering with other radio services. . . ." Nobody can prevent you from assembling and wiring your kit, or removing the chassis from your factory-built job to gloat over and admire. However, you'd better not "fire it up," even for testing, until you have obtained your license and have it in your possession!

7-3. You have probably read or heard about dummy antennas, which are used for testing transmitters with a minimum of interference to others. Even a dummy antenna *will* radiate, although most inefficiently. Such a device would therefore be prohibited for any but duly licensed persons. Nevertheless, after you obtain your license, you will find a dummy antenna most convenient for the various tune-up and adjustment procedures, as well as for troubleshooting. For that reason, we are going to briefly discuss this handy little device.

7-4. The most common dummy "load" in amateur practice is an ordinary electric light bulb of the 115/120 volt variety. These bulbs come in various wattages. Generally, one is chosen with a wattage approximately equal to the input wattage to the plate of the final amplifier. In other words, if the plate power input is 40 watts, a 40-watt lamp is used in the dummy circuit. If the input is 20 watts, a 25-watt bulb is used because it is a common size. The same holds true for any plate power input below 75 watts. If you cannot find a matching bulb, use the next size larger. For example, with a plate power input of 55 watts, use a 60-watt bulb, and so on. The light bulb is connected as shown in Fig. 7-1. You can either solder wires to the lamp base or use a socket.

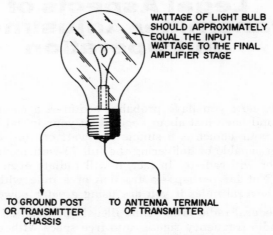

WATTAGE OF LIGHT BULB SHOULD APPROXIMATELY EQUAL THE INPUT WATTAGE TO THE FINAL AMPLIFIER STAGE

TO GROUND POST OR TRANSMITTER CHASSIS

TO ANTENNA TERMINAL OF TRANSMITTER

Fig. 7-1. A simple dummy antenna.

7-5. When the transmitter tuning knob is adjusted to the point where it passes through "resonance," the plate-current meter indication will dip sharply. The lowest point of this dip is the resonant condition. Here the maximum current will be transferred to the antenna. At this dip point the brilliancy of the lamp bulb, used as a dummy load, should be maximum. Most instruction manuals which accompany the kits or assembled transmitters will explain the subject of adjustments at considerable length. You should by all means study these directions if you want optimum operation from the equipment.

7-6. While impatiently awaiting the arrival of the coveted "ticket," why don't you build a permanent dummy load like the one in Fig. 7-2? Although this book is not intended as a construction manual, such a simple project will give you an insight into home construction of ham radio equipment. The cost involved in building this unit is negligible—probably $1.50 if you buy everything! Use of such a dummy load during your testing and troubleshooting will earn you the undying gratitude of your fellow hams, as well as keep you on the right side of the ledger with the FCC!

7-7. Let's now discuss one of the legal requirements you will have to comply with—a portion of the radio laws and regulations which, if violated, can cost you heavy penalties. This is the use of profane or obscene language over the air, which is *absolutely prohibited.* Remember that violation of the rules and regulations of the FCC can result in fines up to $500 for each day the offense occurs, plus suspension of the operator's license and revocation of the station license.

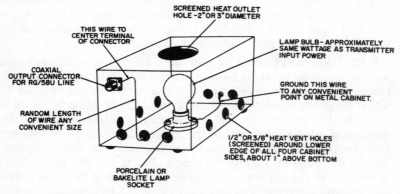

Fig. 7-2. A more elaborate dummy antenna that you can build.

7-8. Another long-standing prohibition concerns the transmission of superfluous signals. It is perhaps a bit difficult to draw the line between "superfluous" and "essential" signals. Were this regulation strictly enforced to the point of splitting hairs, violations by the score would be chalked up daily. For example, a great many novices, particularly in the teen-age group, seem to delight in ending a conversation by sending the characters, *dah-dit-dit-dit-dit,* and waiting for the other fellow to complete the rhythm with *dah-dah.* Such transmission conveys no information or intelligence; therefore, it falls within the superfluity classification. Novices are not alone in this practice; many general class amateurs also do the same. The conscientious ham knows that amateur radio exists because an understanding government appreciates the many contributions the ham fraternity has given technically, as well as the personal services rendered during emergencies. Of course, a light exchange of humor is to be expected in the course of casual conversation, just as in a face-to-face or telephone conversation. There is nothing objectionable to that. The signal "HI," universally employed to express a laugh by radio, is common practice. It is *not* superfluous, since it has a definite meaning.

7-9. What do constitute the more serious offenses in the superfluous group are: (1) holding down the key for long intervals while the antenna is connected to a transmitter; (2) persistent calling of another station known to be communicating with others; (3) practicing sending with a radiating transmitter rather than a buzzer or audio code oscillator—plus similar selfish practices. To these, add sideband splatter from radiophone amateurs, key clicks from CW transmitters, radiation of illegal harmonics of the fundamental frequency, radiation of spurious frequencies inside or outside the amateur bands, and similar "off beat" operation, and you will have a pretty good idea of what constitutes spurious signals. Don't *you* be guilty of any of them!

7-10. You should know by now that, according to federal regulations, a crystal must be used to control the frequency of a novice transmitter. As a novice, you will not be permitted any of the more tempting devices—such as a variable frequency oscillator (VFO)—for generating radio-frequency oscillations at any frequency of your choice within the specified bands. With the variable frequency oscillator, you can transmit on any frequency within its range by merely flipping a dial to the desired point. It *is* difficult to refrain from buying or building one, but *don't* while you are still a novice! The law says you must be *crystal controlled* as long as you remain in this category. Even with a crystal-controlled oscillator, there is no guarantee that your transmissions will be legal, frequencywise. Surprise you? Don't let it! Even the best crystals (within the ham price range) can put out a weak oscillation at a spurious frequency which may not be harmonically related to *any* amateur band. Your 75 watts, misdirected, could knock the props from under some commercial or marine station if it got out of bounds. What's the answer? You'll reduce the gamble substantially by buying a *good* crystal at the start. Shy away from any home-ground jobs. Buy a standard, precision-ground crystal; it is your best assurance that you are within the legal limits of your frequency band. Why gamble with off-frequency operation?

7-11. Next, let us look at probably the most serious violation of federal laws of which you could be guilty. This is one which will almost invariably carry the maximum fine, or imprisonment, or both. We are talking about the transmission of a false distress signal. Unbelievable as it may seem, such things have occurred. Infrequently, thank goodness, but even *one* such call is one too many. It is almost inconceivable that an amateur, or anyone else

80

for that matter, would transmit the international distress signal—"SOS" in the radiotelegraph code; the word "MAYDAY" by radiotelephone—unless an actual emergency existed. But they have! A radio distress call immediately alerts every station hearing it. All other transmission ceases as the concentrated efforts of hundreds or even thousands of competent operators are concentrated on locating the person who has asked for help. What a despicable thing it is to subject so many humans to the hazards of search, and to cause the loss of uncounted thousands of dollars, in a vain effort to locate a false disaster. Is it any wonder that the federal radio law provides the maximum penalty for such hoax transmissions?

7-12. False distress signals are not the only false signals for which the law provides a stiff penalty. Although the consequences may not be quite as severe to the offender, they will approach the seriousness of false distress-signal transmission. Deliberately using the call letters of another station, or those of your own choosing, for example, is one type of false signal. This is known as "bootlegging" in ham circles, and offenders are dealt with severely by the FCC. Another type of false signal is impersonation of some public utility, emergency service, or law-enforcement agency—through use of their call letters and frequency—to divert them from an actual emergency location or send them on a wild-goose chase. The offender might be guilty of *two*, maybe even *three*, violations of federal radio law: (1) transmission of false signals, (2) use of unauthorized call letters, and (3) using a frequency not authorized by the federal radio license.

7-13. Manufacturers of kits and transmitters do everything possible to insure that their products will operate within the legal power limits. Some transmitters in the low-power group are not capable of a power input to the final amplifier tube which would place them outside the legal limits. With them, there is no problem. However, many novices would like to keep the same transmitter, but increase the power input, after they have qualified for their general class license. With this thought in mind, many manufacturers have provided a simple arrangement whereby this can be done. A colored mark on the amplifier plate-current meter scale indicates the maximum plate current the particular transmitter can use under the novice provision. Their instruction books explain fully what antenna loading adjustments must be made in order to keep the final amplifier plate current within this upper limit. Beyond that, they cannot go. You are privileged to purchase a transmitter of any wattage up to 1000 in the way of final amplifier input power. The manufacturer cannot guarantee that you will *operate* under the maximum 75 watts during your novice apprenticeship. He gives you every aid; if you exceed the legal limitation, it is your fault, *not* his.

7-14. Now for a bit of bookkeeping—a record of transmissions, universally referred to as the log of station operations. All amateurs (as well as other services) must keep a log of station operation. By this we do *not* mean you must list every signal you *hear* on the air, but you most certainly must list every *transmission* you make! Remember that the FCC is *not* interested in what you hear: listening can cause no interference with other radio services. However, your transmissions can. So, it is up to you, as an amateur station owner and operator, to keep an accurate and up-to-the-minute record of your transmissions by means of a radio log.

7-15. A considerable number of entries have to be made in the log in order to reflect a clear picture of your transmissions. A quick glance at the requirements may dismay you. Actually, you need not enter every single item listed for each transmission. Let's look at a sheet from a log book available from the American Radio Relay League. (See Fig. 7-3.) The printed columns provide for the essential data required by FCC regulations. This does not mean, however, that you must meticulously enter *every* item on *every* line. The date and time column, sure; you must supply that

DATE TIME 7-30-57	STATION CALLED	CALLED BY	HIS FREQ. OR DIAL	HIS SIGNALS RST	MY SIGNALS RST	FREQ. MC.	EMIS-SION TYPE	POWER INPUT WATTS	TIME OF ENDING QSO	OTHER DATA
0821	CQ	W7OE	—	—	—	3.5	A1	42	0821.3	No Answer
0826	"	W6GF	—	569	579	"	"	"	0853	Rag Chew
0911	W7A13	W7OE	—	579	559	"	"	"	0922	Sent 1 Msg.-Rec'd 2
0953	CQ	"	—	—	—	"	"	"	0953.2	No Ans.-Closed Station W.O.

Fig. 7-3. A typical log sheet.

information. But suppose, while spending a couple of hours in your "shack" some evening, you make a number of "contacts" with other stations. Since the date is the same, you merely enter it once to cover that evening's (or day's) operation. The *time* must be entered for each contact . . . first when you make the contact, again when you finish. The "station called" column is also a must; indicate *whom* you called (by call letters). If *you* were called, perhaps after a "CQ," show who called you, in the third column. The next three columns are not a must; suit yourself if you want to use them. The seventh column, "FREQ. MC," must be filled. Show the frequency *band* (not necessarily the exact frequency) here. If you stay on the same band, ditto marks or a straight line drawn down through the column will do. The type of emission (CW, phone, teletype, or whatever) must be shown in the next column; but if you are working CW only, a simple entry on the first line at the top of the page will do. Change the designation only if you change from phone to CW, or vice versa. If you change back, so indicate in this column opposite the appropriate time.

7-16. The power input in watts must also be shown. However, if your novice transmitter is operating in the 3.5-mc band only, and its normal power consumption is 66 watts, you need show the entry once and ditto it for the rest of the column. If you shift to the 7.0-mc band and your power input changes up or down, say so in your log. The time the QSO was ended must be entered; the FCC wants to know how much time you consumed in the particular QSO—for example, from 7:13 pm (1913 military time) to 8:02 pm (2002). Not that they care how long you talked to the other station. But if some emergency came up in the interim, were you guilty of interfering? Did you hear the emergency call . . . or what *was* your status at the time?

7-17. The column provided for "Other Data" is yours to use freely. Maybe you want to enter the other ham's name or his location; or perhaps a few notes on his equipment—that's up to you. Just remember that the log, which is a record of your operation, is required by FCC regulations. It must be retained for one year after the date of the last entry. It may then be destroyed.

7-18. For portable and/or mobile operation, the ARRL supplies a *Minilog*, a smaller edition of the big book, with smaller pages and fewer columns. Certain entries on the inside front cover take care of a number of formal entries, thus saving space. If you are considering portable or mobile ham operation, it will be to your advantage to read one of the special manuals devoted entirely to that subject. Suffice it to say here that if you intend to operate a mobile or portable station in a location other than that specified on your license for longer than 48 hours, you must notify, in advance, the FCC Engineer-in-Charge of the district in which you intend to operate.

7-19. Here are a few questions on the legal aspects of ham radio, which you must know in order to pass your novice exam.

1. Improper, profane, or obscene language, or false signals, may be transmitted:
   (a) if the power input does not exceed 5 watts   (b) at will   (c) at no time   (d) by radiotelegraph only   ANSWER: (c).

2. Violation of any of the FCC rules and/or regulations is punishable by:
   (a) $10,000 fine and two years' imprisonment   (b) $500 fine   (c) $500 fine and suspension of operator license and revocation of station license   (d) no penalty is provided   ANSWER: (c).

Answer (a) would be incorrect, since that penalty is imposed for violation of federal *laws*, whereas the question pertains to violations of FCC *rules and regulations*. Answer (b) is correct from the monetary standpoint, but neglects to include the license suspension and revocation clauses; it would therefore not be a complete answer to the maximum penalty provided. Obviously, (d) is wrong.

3. How long must the log of an amateur station be preserved?
   (a) 6 months   (b) 12 months   (c) 18 months   (d) 5 years
   ANSWER: (b).

You'll recall that your log sheets must not be destroyed until one year from the date of the last entry. Since they constitute a record of your station operation, they may be valuable in the event of false signals, unlicensed operation, and similar violations by some amateur. Your log sheets could be the evidence required to cinch the case against the violator and keep ham radio the clean hobby it is. Conversely, they can very well establish *your* innocence, should you be falsely accused of some violation.

4. Deliberate interference with other radio communication is:
   (a) permitted if radiotelegraphy is used   (b) prohibited at all times   (c) allowed on frequencies above 220 mc   (d) allowed on radiotelephone   ANSWER: (b).

5. What is the term of an amateur radio novice license?
   (a) 5 years   (b) 6 months   (c) 2 years   (d) 18 months
   ANSWER: (c).

While the novice license was initially established at one year, a later FCC ruling liberalized this to a two year term effective November 22, 1967.

84

6. A novice may operate *radiotelephone* in what band?

Until November 22, 1968 novices were allowed radiotelephone privileges in the 145-147 mc band. Subsequent to that date, radiotelephone operation was prohibited to novice class licenses.

You should remember this from Chapter 6.

7. What method of transmission is indicated by the symbol "CW"?

(a) radiotelegraphy   (b) radiotelephony   (c) facsimile   (d) radioteletype   ANSWER: (a).

Continuous-wave radiotelegraphy, abbreviated CW (covered in Chapter 2) is transmission of intelligence in the form of a radio-frequency carrier broken up into the characters of the radio-telegraph code by manipulation of a hand telegraph key or a semiautomatic code-sending device.

8. What symbol is recognized by FCC as indicating radiotelephony?

(a) CW   (b) kc   (c) A3   (d) A1   ANSWER: (c).

This was discussed in Chapter 6. You will also find a listing of these symbols in the Appendix.

9. If you intend to operate as a portable station at times, you must notify the FCC Engineer-in-Charge of the District in which you propose to operate, if such operation will be for more than:

(a) 24 hours   (b) 30 days   (c) 48 hours   (d) 12 hours ANSWER: (c).

Did you know that, even as a novice, you may take your station with you on a fishing or hunting trip, and operate legally if you comply with the above requirement, and also place a diagonal (/) after your call, followed by the number of the call-letter area in which you are operating? Like this: ". . . DE KN7XXX/6" (if you are operating in the sixth call-letter district). How do you send a "slant bar" in code? Easy! Merely run the letters D and N together like this, DN—or, in *dits* and *dahs*, *dah-dit-dit-dah-dit*. Take another break now with your code-practice gear and really *cram*, for you are now finished with the technical portion of your study.

8

Examination Procedure

8-1. Do you feel ready now to try your luck in the formal examination? You're not too sure? Better check yourself a bit then. First, how about your code ability? There is, of course, no reason why you should request an examination unless you are sure you can copy five five-letter words or groups without error, in one minute. This means—and we want to emphasize it—that the mere fact that you *did* manage to hit five words per minute once or twice during practice is no guarantee that you will do as well under the stress of a formal examination. It matters little who examines you—a friendly neighboring amateur, a qualified stranger or a member of your immediate family—it is still a formal examination and, as such, will have a definite psychological effect on most people. Excess nervous tension is built up which in turn tends to lower your powers of concentration. Five words per minute in code speed is actually ridiculously slow. You would probably make a better showing at ten with a bit more practice, because your mind has less chance to wander between characters. However, five words per minute is the minimum speed required and that is generally what your code examiner will give you. Nothing will prevent you from requesting that he send faster, but remember that it is *you* who are asking for it! You may be jeopardizing your chances of passing if you are overly optimistic, unless you have had previous code experience. Better that you sit down to five words a minute confidently than to ask for eight or ten with misgivings. You should have no difficulty in making pretty solid copy before your examiner at five words a minute. You will have *five* chances; he will send to you continuously for five minutes. You need only show him 25 readable, connected characters *in sequence* anywhere in the series of 125 total characters he sends.

8-2. Now let's consider your *technical* readiness for the examination. The examination questions touch on the technical side so lightly that they can be considered elementary. As we have previously pointed out, a thorough study of this book will give you more than enough knowledge to gain a satisfactory passing grade. Nevertheless, you have nothing to lose and much to gain by reading and studying as much additional material as you can. Current periodicals, plus numerous books and manuals, offer much informative material. Even if you don't have time to really study them, some valuable information will rub off on you— every bit of it an asset to your future ham career. Not only does this added knowledge increase your confidence and ability to pass your novice examination, but it will also benefit you greatly when you appear for a higher grade license at some future time. Bear in mind that you can be a novice for only two years and that a novice license cannot be renewed. At the end of this period (or before if possible), you must qualify for a technician or higher grade of license to remain on the air. Study all that you need to know to procure a license in one of these higher grades. Such a study can be started before you receive your novice license and pursued still further while you are enjoying actual operation of your novice station. In this way you'll be reasonably certain to become an increasingly *good* novice rather than one who has procured his license merely by memorizing a series of answers the meanings of which were either vague or entirely foreign to you.

8-3. We'll now assume that after having given careful thought to the points mentioned in the preceding paragraphs, you still feel sufficiently prepared—both code-wise and technically—to request an examination. How do you go about it? First, address a postal card to the Federal Communications Commission, Gettysburg, Pennsylvania 17325, and request an "Application Form 610 for Amateur Radio Operator and Station License." Sign your name and mailing address and drop it in the nearest mailbox. While you are awaiting the arrival of this application form we suggest that you forget there is such a thing as ham radio for a few days! Go fishing, play golf, or engage in any other activity remote from ham radio. Why? You'll find that after a little break like this you can come back to your study refreshed and ready for your examination.

8-4. Once you've received your application form, look it over carefully before filling it out. As an applicant for a novice license you may disregard the *reverse* side of the form; it applies only to those applicants who are requesting renewal of higher grade licenses which they currently hold. Obviously, as an applicant for your first amateur radio license, you have nothing to renew. Completion of the face of the application form is a simple operation. However, as a guide, a reproduction of a properly executed form using a fictitious name and address, is given in Appendix H. If the information which you enter on your form follows the same pattern, you will be correct. Upon completion, *do not* return this application to FCC. Instead, hold it until you appear for your code test, then hand it to your examiner, who will check it for accuracy and completeness.

8-5. While you are awaiting receipt of your application form from the FCC you should select your examiner. He may be anyone of either sex who is 21 years of age or older and holds a valid amateur radio operator license of the general, advanced, or extra class. In addition, anyone who holds a *commercial* radio*telegraph* license, or is an operator at a U. S. Government radio*telegraph* station, using *manual* telegraphing equipment, can serve as your examiner. You probably know of some friendly amateur or a qualified professional radiotelegraph operator who would be willing to act as your examiner. If you know of none, a local amateur radio club or perhaps one of the amateur radio stores in your vicinity can very likely supply you with the names of several. If you live within an area where a local FCC field office exists, they can probably suggest someone who has indicated a willingness to serve in this capacity. Officially they cannot *assign* such an examiner, since the latter serves voluntarily without compensation. If you are not successful in locating an examiner through any of these means, write to The American Radio Relay League, Inc., 225 Main Street, Newington, Conn., for such information. Anyone agreeing to act as your examiner does so in an entirely voluntary capacity; you, therefore, cannot *demand* that he so serve—you can only *request*. Be courteous and keep in mind that he is doing you a favor. You will find few, if any, who will refuse.

8-6. Suppose now that we get on with the actual examination. If you are satisfied that you have properly completed your application form, contact your examiner and arrange with him for a time and place agreeable to both of you where he can administer the code test. When you appear before him, hand him your application. After he is satisfied that you have executed the form in the proper manner, he will proceed to examine your code receiving ability. He will send to you, either by hand key and buzzer (or audio oscillator), or, if he is so equipped, by means of an automatic tape transmitter. His sending speed will be timed to produce twenty-five radiotelegraph code characters in exactly one minute; this is equal to five five-letter words per minute. The choice of material from which he sends is his. It will be relatively simple; no "trick" characters will be thrown at you. There will probably be a series of letters in the form of simple, pronounceable words such as "dog," "cat," "here," "there," etc. A few figures and an occasional common punctuation mark such as a period, comma, or question mark will likely be introduced, as well as a series of unconnected characters thus: "A F L Z X 2 R M 7 U Z 9" or similar. The better you know the code, the better chance you will have of passing. He will give you *five* chances by sending to you continuously for five consecutive minutes. At the end of that time he must be able to find 25 *readable* characters in consecutive order somewhere among the 125 characters you have written. When we say "readable" we mean just that! Don't scribble some hieroglyphics which only you can interpret! Your handwriting (or printing, if you prefer) must be legible. You cannot use a typewriter however to copy the code test. A typewriter may not always be available to copy messages; too, the noise of the keys can prove a bit distracting. You may use a pencil, ball-point pen, a pen-inholder and a bottle of ink, a paint brush, or even a goose quill dipped in raspberry juice, just as long as it is readable!

8-7. You passed your receiving test with all flags flying (we hope!). The code is not behind you yet, however. Next comes a test of your "fist"—your ability to *send*. You won't have the privilege of using an automatic tape machine or even a semiautomatic "bug" key. Although your examiner can use any commonly accepted code transmitting device which he may choose, *you* are going to have to place your "paw" on the knob of a conventional hand key and show proficiency in *sending* equal to what we hope you showed in receiving—namely, five words per minute. Take it easy! Five words per minute is so slow that you can almost take a short nap between characters if you know the code. There is no earthly need for you to grab the key knob as if it will run out the door the minute you relax your grip! As we explained in Chapter 2, there *is* no grip which should be forced on you. Hold the key in a relaxed manner—one which is most comfortable to you. Nothing in the radio laws or regulations prescribes *how* you must hold the key knob; just make good, readable code with either hand in any manner you desire.

8-8. Your examiner may or may not hand you some material from which to send. It may be a short item from a newspaper, or something he has written down himself, or it may be the nameplate data from a piece of ham equipment. What he wants is to hear your character formation at a minimum speed of five words a minute and your knowledge of mixed groups—some letters, a few words, several scattered figures and simple punctuation, and perhaps a short sentence or two, similar to what he sent to you.

He may not even hold you for the full five minutes if it is obvious to him that you are qualified. Don't tense up; just coast along at five or six words a minute making good, clean, sharp, and solid characters. If he stops your sending after two or three minutes, you can just about figure that you've made it. If he lets you run the full five minutes, cross your fingers. He is being completely fair with you and if he has detected a few errors here and there as you proceeded, he'll give you a chance to make up for them by letting you continue for the full five minutes. Just keep trying right to the end; perhaps your performance will improve; it frequently does in the last minutes as your confidence increases. However, if he doesn't find 25 consecutive, readable characters in your five-minute run, he has no choice but to say, "Sorry, Bud, I'm afraid you didn't make it. You'd better practice more on your sending and I'll be glad to see you again in thirty days." Thirty days is the minimum period required before you can appear for re-examination; this should give you ample time to improve your sending. If you don't make it on the second try, go after it again in another thirty days. You can continue to re-appear at thirty-day intervals indefinitely; eventually you'll make it, so stick with it. Go back and read Chapter 2 again, especially where we stress the necessity for learning code at a somewhat *greater* speed than the examination requires. Study and practice until you can whip it out at a good, steady six to eight words a minute, both sending and receiving, and you'll do all right.

8-9. We'll take it for granted that you passed your code test both ways; what next? Your examiner will then write a letter to the Federal Communications Commission at Gettysburg, Pa., and request the examination papers for the novice-class examination. His letter must include the following information:

1. The names and mailing addresses of both himself as examiner and you as the applicant.
2. A description of his qualifications to administer the examination. (This merely means that he will state the class and serial number of the valid amateur radio license which he currently holds, or a statement to the effect that he has a valid commercial radio*telegraph* operator license or is employed in the service of the United States Government as a radiotelegraph operator using manually operated radiotelegraph equipment.)
3. His statement that you have passed the required code test within ten days prior to the date of his letter and the submission of your application.
4. His written signature.

He will then attach his letter to your application and forward both to the Gettysburg office of the FCC. Upon receipt of your application and the accompanying letter, the FCC will forward the written examination papers directly to him, not to you. He will notify you of their receipt and you can then make arrangements with him for the time and place where he will conduct the examination. This should be at as early a date as practical commensurate with your mutual convenience. The FCC requires that the completed examination papers be returned to them within 20 days from the date on which they forwarded them to your examiner.

8-10. When you appear for examination, deliver to the examiner a 6″ × 9″ manila envelope (available at most stationery or novelty stores) which you have previously addressed to "Federal Communications Commission, Gettysburg, Pa. 17325," and bearing the return address of the examiner. You should insert within the envelope a medium-weight piece of cardboard, approximately 5½″ × 8½″, to serve as a stiffener. (Your answer sheet must be returned to FCC without folding, stapling or otherwise mutilating.) A piece cut from a cardboard grocery carton will be quite suitable as a stiffener. The envelope should be prominently marked on the outside "DO NOT FOLD OR BEND," and sufficient first-class postage attached to insure delivery. Your examiner will then open the examination envelope that he has received from FCC and remove the contents in your presence. He will hand both the envelope and the enclosed examination papers to you. You should first read the instructions printed on the face of the envelope (Fig. 8-1). Next write your name on *each* page of the examination; then complete Part I on the back of the answer sheet. If you are claiming no code element credit (allowed only if you now hold or have previously held a commercial radio*telegraph* license), you may ignore item 1 of Part I, but you must complete and sign item 2 in its entirety. You may now proceed with the examination proper. Read the questions over thoroughly first. When you feel that you are ready to mark your answers, do so carefully in the manner prescribed on the answer sheet (Fig. 8-2). After completing all of your answers, go over them again. There may be something which you would like to change; feel free to do so, but any erasures or changes must be neatly done and each should be initialed to indicate that you, personally, have made such changes.

8-11. All through? Fine! It took you only thirty-five minutes (the average time is about 45 minutes) and the way you were chewing your pencil gave the impression that you were really in

APPLICANT

FEDERAL COMMUNICATIONS COMMISSION
United States of America

WRITTEN EXAMINATION
For N O V I C E C L A S S
AMATEUR OPERATOR PRIVILEGES

Serial Number_____

CAUTION: ANY ATTEMPT TO OBTAIN AN OPERATOR LICENSE BY FRAUDULENT MEANS OR BY ATTEMPTING TO IMPERSONATE ANOTHER, OR BY COPYING OR DIVULGING QUESTIONS USED IN EXAMINATIONS, OR REFERRING TO NOTES, WILL CONSTITUTE A VIOLATION OF THE REGULATIONS, FOR WHICH PENALTIES ARE PROVIDED.

TO THE VOLUNTEER EXAMINER:

This envelope contains the written examination for an amateur radio operator license which is being entrusted to you at your request and upon your showing of your qualifications to supervise an examination for the above named applicant. As the Volunteer Examiner, you are necessarily required to assume responsibility for the proper disposition of these examination papers and for the proper conduct of the examination. Your assistance and cooperation in this regard are considered absolutely vital to the success of the examination-by-mail program. Your supervision of this examination must be in accordance with the following procedure:

A – DO NOT OPEN THIS ENVELOPE but return it to the Commission if the examination is not taken within 20 days from the date you receive it or if, for any other reason, you are unable to administer the examination (furnish an explanation).

B – Open this envelope in the presence of the applicant at the time he is to take the examination and perform the following steps:

1. Insure that the applicant reads the instructions on this envelope, that he signs his name on each page of the examination, and that he completes PART I on the back of the Answer Sheet.

2. Insure that no outside reference material or assistance is utilized by the applicant during the examination. The examination must be completed without interruption within a reasonable time in your presence.

3. Terminate the examination immediately for any impropriety and report the circumstances to the Commission.

4. Complete PART II on the back of the Answer Sheet when the applicant has completed the examination.

5. Upon completion or termination of the examination, immediately forward all examination papers and the Answer Sheet to the Federal Communications Commission, Gettysburg, Pennsylvania 17325, using a stamped envelope furnished by the applicant. DO NOT FOLD, STAPLE OR MUTILATE THE ANSWER SHEET.

INSTRUCTIONS TO THE APPLICANT:

A – Comply with the instructions of the Volunteer Examiner.

B – Sign your name on each page of the examination papers and complete PART I on the back of the Answer Sheet.

C – Use of any reference material or outside assistance during the examination is absolutely forbidden. The examination will be terminated by the Volunteer Examiner for any impropriety in its conduct.

D – Each examination question lists five answers from which you must choose one and only one which you consider to be the correct answer. Use a soft lead pencil for your answers. On the Answer Sheet fill in the space having the same letter as that of your choice for the correct answer. If more than one space is filled in for the same question, the answer will be marked wrong.

E – When the examination is completed or terminated, hand all examination papers to the volunteer examiner, together with a stamped envelope for the return of the examination. DO NOT FOLD, STAPLE OR MUTILATE THE ANSWER SHEET.

2¾-M 11-63

Fig. 8-1. Instructions on the envelope of the novice examination.

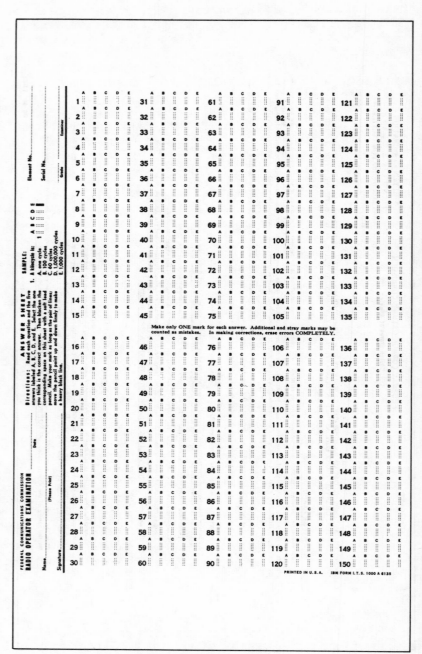

Fig. 8-2. The answer sheet for the license exam.

there pitching—let's hope you were. When you're positive that you have done your best, hand all of your papers to your examiner. He will complete Part II on the reverse of your answer sheet and sign it and will then place the question sheets and your answer in the large envelope which you have previously supplied him, seal it, and it's ready to be mailed. Now the waiting game begins. After a few days you will probably begin to fidget. You must resign yourself to the fact that it is going to take awhile before you hear the results. FCC has scores of these examinations to check daily and they are done in sequence; it may be four, six or even eight weeks before you hear the outcome of your examination. We know that you are anxious to receive your license and we don't blame you. Just be patient, though; the FCC is working just as fast as it can to get you on the air (if you've passed). In the meantime you can spend your odd moments setting up your equipment in readiness to go right into business when the coveted ticket arrives. Don't burden FCC with inquiries as to when you may expect it; such just clutter up their mail basket and could introduce more delay.

8-12. We are going to digress here to clear up a point which may have puzzled you. You have probably noticed that we mentioned a "filing fee" occasionally in preceding chapters. Your application form also carries a notation: "Enclose appropriate fee with application if required." To clarify this, until just recently there has been no cost in connection with procurement of any license. However, early in 1964 a schedule of fees was set up for all civilian radio services, including the amateur class. However, the novice class of amateurs were exempted from any fee whatsoever and, at this writing, none is required. You should therefore include *no* payment of any kind with your application. In the event that such fees should eventually include the novice class, prominent publicity will be given to such action in the pages of the electronic and amateur radio magazines.

8-13. Now, to see how well you have studied this chapter, suppose we try a few questions on which to test yourself.

1. When you feel ready to appear for a formal FCC examination, what is your first step?
   (a) write FCC requesting Form 610, Application for Amateur Radio Operator and Station License   (b) ask FCC to send you a license as a novice radio amateur   (c) request FCC to send an engineer to examine you   (d) appear at an FCC field office for examination
   ANSWER: (a).

2. If an amateur applicant fails an examination, what is the waiting period before he can appear for re-examination?
   (a) 1 year   (b) 6 months   (c) 90 days   (d) 30 days   ANSWER: (d).

3. How soon after taking your examination can you engage in actual on-the-air operation?

(a) you can immediately commence transmitting operation (b) you can transmit at once on radiotelegraph only (c) you must await receipt of your formal license from the FCC (d) you can immediately operate on radiotelephone only ANSWER: (c).

4. Your examiner is selected by:

(a) yourself (b) your local FCC field office (c) the Gettysburg headquarters of the FCC (d) your local amateur club ANSWER: (a).

5. What is the filing fee for novice class applications?

(a) currently none (b) $1.00 (c) $4.00 (d) $5.00 ANSWER: (a).

9

Assembling Your Station

9-1. This book is not intended as a "construction manual"; no attempt is made to tell you how to build equipment other than one or two minor accessory items. We do, however, want to offer you some suggestions and advice on *choosing* proper equipment for your initial entry into the ham ranks and in arranging it in a neat and convenient manner.

9-2. Perhaps you have already acquired a communications receiver as we suggested in Chapter 2. If so, one major cost item is behind you. We will assume that you have also procured a pair of headphones with the receiver. As stated in Chapter 2, you will find it easier to concentrate on copying code with headphones than with a speaker. The phones act as "ear muffs" and shut out room noises —conversation and other extraneous sounds which would otherwise distract you. The receiver in Fig. 9-1 is ideal for the novice. It sells for about $120 and will serve you for many years after you obtain your general license.

9-3. If you have not as yet acquired a communications receiver, be guided in your choice through the advice of a more experienced ham. This is especially desirable if you are considering a used receiver or one of the military surplus types. With such guidance from a friendly amateur and the budget restrictions of your wallet, you are ready to purchase this very essential item of station equipment. If you choose a *used* receiver, particularly one of the military types, be *sure* that an original instruction book is included with it; without such, you will be a "wheel without a wagon."

9-4. Choosing a transmitter should be next in line. Here, too, the advice of a more skilled amateur is valuable. Whether you choose to purchase a new or used transmitter is, of course, up to you. If it is a new one that you are contemplating, choose one made by a well-known factory whose reputation for reliable quality

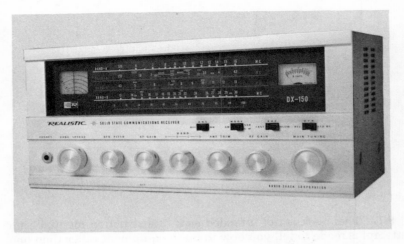

Courtesy The Radio Shack Corp.

Fig. 9-1. A modern communication receiver of the solid-state type is represented by this Realistic DX-150.

has been well established. The 50-watt transmitter in Fig. 9-2 sells for under $50.00 in kit form. This unit is representative of the many high-quality transmitters available to the novice.

9-5. You have two choices in selecting a new transmitter; you can buy one already assembled, wired, and tested by the factory or you can purchase one in kit form which you can assemble yourself. Fortunately, strange as it may seem, transmitter kits in the novice class are far less complicated to assemble and wire than a

Courtesy Allied Radio Corp.

Fig. 9-2. The Knight-Kit Model T-60 transmitter.

good communications receiver (see Fig. 9-3). There are fewer parts in a transmitter so the components are not bunched closely together as in the better receivers. Furthermore, no touchy alignment procedures are required. You won't find it difficult to put such a kit together and accomplish the wiring if you stick religiously to the instructions contained in the assembly manual accompanying it. Do *not* deviate; every step is laid out for you and should be accomplished in the order indicated in the instructions.

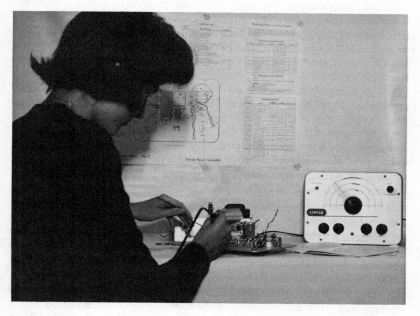

Fig. 9-3. This young lady is wiring the front panel of a Conar 400 novice radio transmitter. The completed companion Conar 500 receiver is shown at the right.

9-6. Kit assembly and wiring requires only a few tools. You can accomplish a good job on the average kit with a small- and medium-size screwdriver, a pair of long-nose and a pair of diagonal-cutting pliers, and a small 35- to 50-watt soldering iron. Complete soldering instructions are contained in all kit assembly manuals to guide you in the event you have had no previous experience in soldering techniques; it is really simple after you have tried your hand at it with a few random pieces of hook-up wire.

9-7. So far, we have discussed only new, factory-assembled and wired transmitters, and new kits. (Obviously you can hardly buy a "used" kit, unassembled!) Suppose though you feel that a *used* transmitter will better fit your budget. The same care should be practiced in shopping for a used transmitter as given previously for a used receiver. We want to caution you though, do not consider a "home-made" used transmitter; this also applies to used receivers. Many amateur constructors turn out some very acceptable gear, either of their own design or from something published in a magazine or handbook. However, you would be in somewhat of a quandary if the need should arise to troubleshoot or repair a piece of home-built equipment. Unfortunately, relatively few ham builders supply any data with the gear which they offer for sale—often not even a schematic. Another distinct liability which this type of equipment is handicapped with, is that it has little or no trade-in or resale value. Occasionally it can be disposed of to an individual ham, but it is generally done so at pretty much of a sacrifice price. Stick to standard, factory-made equipment. A used piece of equipment assembled from a well-known kit is, however, generally a satisfactory item to buy provided it has not been modified by the builder. Any modifications will void your chances of a trade-in with most of the electronic stores and mail-order houses. Regardless of what you may choose in a used transmitter, insist that the original factory instruction book be included with it. This is particularly important if you buy surplus equipment; they are often lacking such a book and they are difficult to obtain.

9-8. Having acquired your major equipment items—the receiver and transmitter—you can pick up the more minor pieces of accessory equipment. The antenna should be next. While we include this as a "minor" item, we are applying this term only because we recommend that you start your "on-the-air" career with the simplest type—a single wire fed either at one end, in the center, or somewhere along its length with a similar single wire. After you have gained experience you may wish to try a more elaborate antenna system such as a doublet, inverted-V, a loaded or trapped vertical, or others. Perhaps you will want to try coaxial cable or a two-wire open line as a feeder to the antenna. Let such departures wait; you'll do a very satisfactory job in your initial communications with just a plain random length of wire between two supports approximately 50 to 75 feet apart. For this antenna you'll need about 100 feet of stranded copper antenna wire. The commonly available seven-strand No. 22 wire is fine and sells for approximately 1½¢ a foot. You'll also need two or three insulators (depending upon how you arrange your antenna run). Any of the small, glazed-porcelain types selling for about a dime apiece are completely satisfactory for the transmitter power you can use as a novice (75 watts). To bring the lead-in wire through a wall or window to the transmitter location, use your ingenuity.

A simple porcelain electrical tube through a hole in the wall (if the landlord isn't looking!) or in a narrow board fitted below or above a double-hung window is fine. Many other suggestions will be found in various handbooks; you'll probably dream up something of your own anyway!

9-9. You can support your antenna between two poles, between a pole and a house gable, or between a pole or house gable and a tree—any way which will get the antenna up as high as possible. (35 to 40 feet at one or both ends). Keep the lead-in clear of contact with tree limbs, house projections, or other obstructions. The sketch in Fig. 9-4 gives a number of ideas for arrangement; many

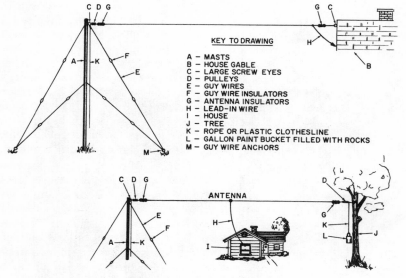

KEY TO DRAWING

A – MASTS
B – HOUSE GABLE
C – LARGE SCREW EYES
D – PULLEYS
E – GUY WIRES
F – GUY WIRE INSULATORS
G – ANTENNA INSULATORS
H – LEAD-IN WIRE
I – HOUSE
J – TREE
K – ROPE OR PLASTIC CLOTHESLINE
L – GALLON PAINT BUCKET FILLED WITH ROCKS
M – GUY WIRE ANCHORS

Fig. 9-4. Various methods of mounting the antenna wire.

more are given in handbooks and magazines. If you plan to use a pole of more than 15 feet, you'll need to guy it with three wires half way up and three at the top. Galvanized iron wire (No. 14) is excellent for guys and also very inexpensive at your local hardware. Break the guys into thirds by inserting insulators, preferably of the little egg-shaped glazed porcelain type. The insulators for all six guys won't cost you more than a dollar at your electronics supply store.

9-10. With the antenna problem now out of the way, suppose we look at the few interior accessories you will need in your station. First, of course, is a hand telegraph key. We can probably skip this here as you no doubt acquired one early in your code practice. We hope you got a good one; if so it can now take its place as your station key. If you still have to buy one, $1.00 to $1.50 will get you a good used one; $2 to $3, a new one. Headphones, if you don't already have them, will run you anywhere from $2 to $5; electrically one is as good as another if you buy them new. Be sure though that they are of at least 2000-ohms impedance. Mechanical features and adjustability of the headband generally account for those in the upper price brackets.

9-11. The lightning arrestor is an accessory too often overlooked not only by the beginner but also by those with experience. This

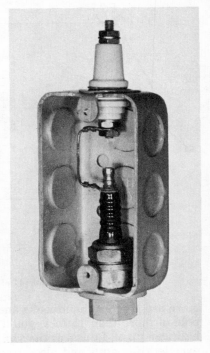

(A) Completed unit.	(B) Interior view.

Fig. 9-5. A lightning arrestor for a single-wire antenna made from a spark plug and an electrical utility box.

is a purely safety feature. It adds nothing to the *operation* of your equipment but it is highly desirable to provide some measure of protection to your gear and often to your home or shack during heavy lightning storms. For a single-wire antenna and lead in, you can make an excellent lightning arrestor for less than a dollar, using a discarded automobile spark plug and an electrical utility

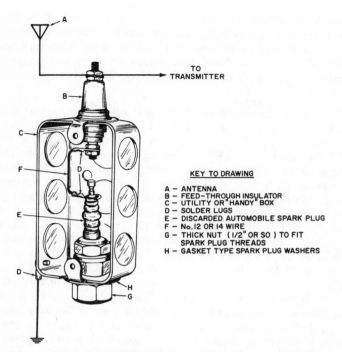

KEY TO DRAWING

A — ANTENNA
B — FEED-THROUGH INSULATOR
C — UTILITY OR "HANDY" BOX
D — SOLDER LUGS
E — DISCARDED AUTOMOBILE SPARK PLUG
F — No. 12 OR 14 WIRE
G — THICK NUT (1/2" OR SO) TO FIT
     SPARK PLUG THREADS
H — GASKET TYPE SPARK PLUG WASHERS

Fig. 9-6. Construction details of spark-plug lightning arrestor.

or "handy" box. Fig. 9-5 shows two views of the unit and Fig. 9-6 shows the construction details. If you later plan to use coaxial cable for an antenna feeder, or "transmission line" as it is more technically known, the Cush Craft *Blitz-Bug* (Fig. 9-7) is admirable and costs little. A single-wire feeder can also be connected to the center pole (blade) of a simple single-pole, double-throw knife switch. The transmitter is connected to one of the switch jaws and the other jaw is connected to a good ground (cold-water pipe or ground rod). When in the grounded-jaw position the transmitter is disconnected and the antenna is connected to

Fig. 9-7. The Cush Craft *Blitz-Bug* lightning arrestor.

Courtesy Cush Craft.

103

ground. Atmospheric discharges will then be bled off to ground unless you get a direct lightning hit—such a hit would probably make a shambles of your home or shack anyway. This type switch sells for 35¢ to 50¢ at hardware stores or electrical shops; just remember to throw it to the ground position when you are not using your equipment.

9-12. A good timepiece is a vital and often overlooked item of accessory equipment. You may think it strange that we consider such a common-place thing as a conventional household clock, as "vital." Remember that FCC regulations require you to log all transmissions by date *and* time. They also insist that you identify your station with your call letters at not more than ten-minute intervals. Without an accurate time piece you cannot comply with these requirements. A wrist watch, spring-wound alarm clock, or a conventional wall- or desk-type electric clock will all serve the purpose, but these all have definite limitations for radio use. You will at least expect to work coast-to-coast, which involves time in the three other zones. Beyond doubt you will want to work hams at even more distant points. Most of these foreign contacts will have time differing considerably from the U. S. zones. It will take a bit of figuring to establish time difference between your station and your foreign contact if he wants to make a schedule with you and uses his own time with which to establish it. Why add the burden of scratching it out each time when you can have it done automatically and instantaneously for you by choosing a suitable clock? An elaborate clock combined with a 15″ × 22″ full-color world map is pictured in Fig. 9-8. The time for 70 key cities, including your local time and all time zones in the world, can be read instantly from this unit. It is available from World of Time, Inc., 1677 Cody Avenue, Queens 10027, New York and sells for $59.95.

9-13. The very minimum in a special clock for ham radio work is one with an electrical movement and with a dial divided into 24 rather than 12 hourly divisions. This is known as a "24-hour train" clock, and is made by several manufacturers in various wall and desk types. Fig. 9-9 shows the *Call-Ident Tymeter* manufactured by Penwood Numechron Co., Pittsburg, Pennsylvania. It has the additional feature of a 10-minute repeating timer to warn you to sign your call letters. This clock is available in walnut, ebony, and ivory, and sells for under $25.00. Other manufacturers have similar units. The Hamilton Watch Company even make a 22-jewel, 24-hour pocket watch (Fig. 9-10), which is ideal for mobile amateur radio operations! The main advantage in using 24-hour timing as used by most military and naval branches is

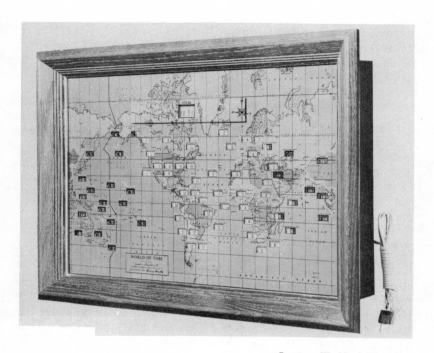

Fig. 9-8. A novel clock combined with a world map.

Fig. 9-9. The Call-Ident *Tymeter* Clock with 10-minute repeating timer.

Fig. 9-10. The Hamilton Navigational Master watch.

Courtesy Hamilton Watch Co.

that when a foreign contact tells you he will see you again at "0230Z" he means 2:30 A.M. GMT. Should he say, "1900Z" it would mean 7:00 P.M. GMT. With a 24-hour clock you need to know only the time differential between you and GMT. Then you can glance at the time shown on your clock and figure the time he plans to call you.

9-14. A simple 24-hour dial offers a more convenient timing arrangement than the conventional 12-hour dial; however, you still have to do some figuring to determine the time in your local time zone in relation to that of the foreign station. Recognizing this, a number of manufacturers offer such clocks with dials indicating the different time zones of the world as well. You can tell at a glance just what time it is locally in any time zone of the United States and in all of the countries of the world! Two of these are illustrated in Figs. 9-11 and 9-12. The one in Fig. 9-11 is available from Novelty Clock Co., P. O. Box 159, Hilliard, Florida. It can be purchased with the case and removable crystal ($15.00), without case and crystal ($12.00), or the dial can be purchased without the motor ($2.00). The unit in Fig. 9-12 is unique in that the dial rather than the hands revolve. It is available from International Time Indicator Co., P. O. Box 165, Albany, New York 12201, ($11.95) and instantly gives the time for any point in the world.

9-15. One other accessory item may or may not be needed—an antenna changeover switch. Many hams prefer to use the same antenna for both transmission and reception. To do so, you must have some means for switching between "send" and "receive."

A simple knife switch is excellent. If you want to try your construction ability in a minor way, you can use a rotary, panel-mounted, single-pole, two-position switch, mounted in a small metal cabinet. Connect the antenna to the center arm of the switch, the transmitter to one contact, and the receiver to the other. If you want to combine your lightning ground switch with your antenna changeover, use a *three*-position rotary switch and connect

Courtesy Novelty Clock Co.

Fig. 9-11. A wall or table clock with 24-hour electric movement and world-time dial.

the third contact to ground. If you prefer to use separate antennas for your transmitter and receiver, a switch is not needed. The receiving antenna can be the same as that described for the transmitter. Any random length of wire, 40 to 60 feet long and 20 to 35 feet high, will serve nicely.

9-16. The foregoing tips and suggestions just about cover all of the equipment you will need initially. Fig. 9-13 shows a typical modest station for the beginning amateur. The Knight-Kit® *Space Spanner* receiver on the left and the Eico Model 723-K sixty-watt transmitter on the right were home assembled from kits. The antenna switch in the center is home constructed. The total cost of

Courtesy International Time Indicator Co.

Fig. 9-12. A novel international standard-time indicator.

the equipment pictured, including the key and headphones, is less than $100. A station like this is capable of world-wide communications. Forget, for a few months at least, such frills as antenna tuners, automatic or semiautomatic keys, keying monitors, coax switches, and the myriad of other accessory devices nationally

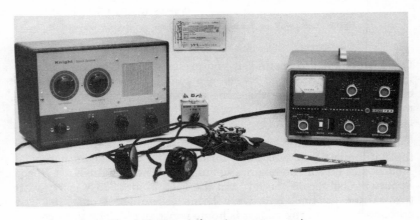

Fig. 9-13. A typical novice amateur station.

advertised. In most cases, they provide only convenience; they contribute nothing to your operating skill. Concentrate only on improving your proficiency in code and in studying the technical angles of equipment design and performance; you hope to take the general class license examination within your "two years of grace"—start preparing for it now! Let the nonessential gadgets of station equipment wait until the general-class license card occupies a prominent place on your wall!

10

"You're on the Air!"

10-1. Imagine the thrill you'll experience when you receive the envelope bearing the impressive return address of the Federal Communications Commission and containing your official license card! You will be the proud owner of an amateur radio station identified by official United States government-assigned call letters! This means that the federal government recognizes you as fully competent to operate a novice amateur radio station.

10-2. Don't fall down the basement stairs as you rush to that ham shack which you've already put together! You can't wait to throw the "big switch." Impatiently you sit for 30 seconds; well, maybe 10, anyway, while your tubes warm up. Then you stick your "fist" into the air lanes! Although probably awkward, stumbling and hesitant, you somehow manage to get a CQ of sorts on the air. And then you listen, carefully tuning your chosen band. (The 80-meter or 3.5-mc band is the best place to start.) Several signals can be heard, none sounding as if they might be calling *you*. But wait! Doesn't that combination of code characters have a familiar ring? Sure enough, loud and clear, comes "KN5YYY DE KN5XXX"! What to do? What did you do when you hooked your first trout? You fought it out with him! Well, go on and fight it out with this KN5XXX who's asking for it! Give it back to him as he gave it to you. Give him your "handle" (ham jargon for name), your location, and how his signals sound to you (using the RST method in Appendix G). That's enough for the first round. It will probably be all you can make on the key anyway, considering the nervous tension you have doubtless developed during your first transmission! Now switch to your receiver and listen. There he is, actually replying. He's sending slowly. You pick up quite a few letters here and there and a few short words. You seem to relax a bit as he goes along . . . it isn't nearly as bad as you had anticipated. Suddenly you recognize his signing-off signals followed by the silence that means, "It's your turn now." You rapidly scan the notes you've made. It seems that he had reported your signals but you're not sure just what he said. His name was Jim—you got that easily—and he lives in Murdock, Texas, although you're not sure of this. Nevertheless, the next move is yours and although the other guy (or gal) has a normal amount of patience, he isn't going to wait too long for your reply.

10-3. So, give him an answer but *don't* do it *this* way: "KN5XXX DE KN5YYY R R R OK OK OM EXCEPT I AM NOT SURE WHERE YOU ARE OR WHAT MY SIGNAL REPORT WAS PLEASE REPEAT." "R" by itself means "all received OK." You didn't get it *all* if you are doubtful of his location and your signal report. Don't be the least bit bashful about telling him that you missed some words—so did he on his first contact (and probably many following ones!). So simply go back to him something like this: "KN5XXX DE KN5YYY BT TNX FOR CALL JIM I GOT YOUR NAME OK AND THINK YOU SAID YOU WERE IN MURDOCK TEXAS BUT AM NOT SURE BT PLEASE REPEAT THAT AND MY SIG REPORT BT THIS IS MY FIRST CONTACT JIM AS JUST GOT MY TICKET BT WEA HR FB HW R?."*

10-4. By the time all that is over with, probably with a half dozen errors and repeats, you begin to feel as though you had been born with a key in your fist. Don't let it throw you! Almost everyone in the novice class goes through a similar grueling experience on his first contact. Jim isn't going to feel hurt if you simply call it quits right then and there. Perhaps he'll call back and give you the repeats you want. If you're still not able to take them, Jim either stays with you and keeps on trying or simply shrugs it off, remembering *his* first few contacts, and looks for a more experienced novice. Don't be discouraged; just dive in and keep on pitching. Your confidence will rapidly increase as you copy more and more of what the other fellow says. It won't be long before you say to yourself, "What's so hard about ham radio?" Your thoughts may even turn toward eventually becoming a commercial radio operator—a slick way to earn a living! hat will be the correct attitude, the stimulant you need. Now just keep going. Improvement, even though slow perhaps, will be steady. Before you know it you'll be thinking, "Why do I have to wait to take the general examination? I've been a novice for several months. I've studied, I'm doing fine in code. So I guess I'll go after the ticket that gives me *all* of the privileges of hamdom."

---

* See Appendix E for abbreviations.

10-5. Now that you've been through the mill with your first contact, perhaps you've found that some little rearrangement of your equipment would make for better operating convenience. Maybe you're left-handed, for example. You've probably mounted your key initially where it is handy to your left hand. But what about your transmitter and receiver? Customarily, for a right-handed ham, the receiver is on the left as shown in Fig. 10-1. This arrangement allows the operator to follow any little drift in an incoming signal by tuning with his left hand while copying with

Fig. 10-1. The Johnson Viking transmitter (recently discontinued) and the National NC-105 receiver.

his right. Not so for the "south-paw" operator! He can't write with his left hand and alternate between his pencil and his tuning dial. The obvious is dictated; put the receiver on the *right!* That places the transmitter, which should never require adjustment during an operating period unless changing bands or crystals, on the *left* for the south-paw, to the *right* for the right-handed guy. If you've got your cart where the horse ought to be, reverse it! If space is limited you can often stack the transmitter and receiver as shown in Fig. 10-2.

10-6. How about your clock? Is it located so that you can conveniently see it for the frequent log entries you'll be making or do you have to turn your head? If so, find a more suitable place for it. Maybe your antenna changeover switch is mounted so that you have to stretch a bit each time you switch between send and receive; relocate it to a handier position. The same for your grounding switch (if you use one for lightning protection); put it where you will remember to ground the antenna when you are not using your gear. Do you have a handy trough or holder for your pencils or do they roll all around your operating table? Do something about it. Make sure that you have sufficient desk space

Fig. 10-2. Transmitter (Knight-Kit Model T-60) mounted on top of receiver (National Model NC-105).

Fig. 10-3. How not to set up your shack!

for convenience in making notes and entries in your log. Make yourself a little bulletin board of celotex or similar soft material to which you can thumb-tack schedules and other pertinent information such as an RST signal chart, a list of Q signals and one for commonly-used ham abbreviations. Mount the board in a position permitting easy visibility.

10-7. Above all, pay particular attention to neatness; always have your station presentable. You'll have many visitors—relatives, friends, and fellow novices will be dropping in frequently. Show them that you are a good housekeeper and that you take pride in presenting the equipment in which you have an investment of many dollars, to best advantage. Pay attention to all of the points which we have made in the preceding paragraphs and you'll turn up with a station on whose wall you will be proud to display your license and call-letter card! Whatever you do, avoid setting up a station like the one in Fig. 10-3. While this photo has been purposely exaggerated, some look almost this bad. Orderly, neat arrangement of equipment is a must in any shack.

11

Operating Procedure

11-1. You've entered the ranks of the grandest hobby in the world—the great international fraternity of radio hams! To really belong, you're going to have to go along with the standard operating procedures universally accepted by radio amateurs. There is really only *one* way for a novice to acquire the proper procedure— by studying the printed text. Your opinion may be that all you need to do is imitate the other novices on the air. You're wrong! Unless they have studied an authoritative text, they are probably operating like fellow novices whom they copied during their early on-the-air operations. The procedures used by the general class operators might seem to be more professional. That is true, except that most general hams will be sending at speeds way over your head. Hence, you have no other recourse except to study proper procedure and follow the book. Don't be a carbon copy of the first few novices you hear or work.

11-2. The most glaring examples of improper procedure are (1) overworking the period, (2) excessively long CQ's, and (3) butchering the DE. The general class of amateur, hearing such awkwardness from another general class station, knows immediately that the other fellow has just acquired his higher grade license, but is still using incorrect, novice methods. It is discouraging to the latter to find his calls going unanswered after he has dropped the novice "N" from his call letters. Novice methods in the general bands are the reason!

11-3. Let's look first at the period. It is such a long combination of dots and dashes—*dit-dah-dit-dah-dit-dah*—just to make a dot on a piece of paper! A long time ago, it used to be *dit-dit dit-dit dit-dit*. This was simpler and hence faster. Why it was ever changed, we'll never know. Many general and extra class operators, although competent in the code otherwise, have to think twice when they hear that string of *A's*, so seldom do they use it. In fact, there is really no occasion to in a casual convertion. Almost anything will do to break the thought. Some simply say *dit-dit dit-dit;* some, the letter *X;* others even use the double dash, $\overline{BT}$. Which one you use is immaterial; it serves merely as a separator between thoughts. Let's try an actual communication: ". . . WELL OM WE HV SURE BEEN HVG FB WX HR $\overline{BT}$ DID YOU SAY YOU WORKED FOR THE TELFO CO? . . ." See how the $\overline{BT}$ separated the thoughts? A period would do. But try them both on your key—which has the greater *rhythm?* After you become a journeyman with your general license, you can forget you ever heard of a period. Of course, you should be able to recognize it on the rare occasions when you'll hear it. However, there is no real reason for an amateur to use this character—even in such a formal communication as a third-party message, complete with heading, address, text, and signature. Commercial operators, who handle thousands of messages a month, use the letter *X* for a period. Let's look at the text of a short message: ". . . BILL AND SHIRLEY ARRIVED TO-DAY X GRANDPA AND GRANDMA DUE NEXT WEEK X LOVE. . . ."

11-4. Now about excessive CQing. The signal, CQ, means the operator is on the air, anxious for a contact. General ham practice has developed the "three-by-three" system: "CQ CQ CQ DE W7OE W7OE W7OE CQ CQ CQ DE W7OE W7OE W7OE CQ CQ CQ DE W7OE W7OE W7OE." In other words, CQ three times, DE once, and your call letters three times—the sequence being repeated three times. Then listen for several minutes before repeating your CQ. The other fellow may be searching wildly through his modest supply of crystals for one close enough to your frequency to attract your attention. However, when you get into the general class, you will be able to send nearly three times as many CQ's at thirteen words per minute as you can at five. Few generals will stick it out while you go through too long a rigamarole. Therefore, send your three-by-three CQ's for no longer than 20 seconds! Remember that the hams who will hear you are experienced. They can tune in your signal faster than a novice. Equipped with a VFO, they need only spin a wheel to land right on your frequency. They have no assortment of crystals to check over while you "beat the anvil." If you keep pounding for a full minute, they may not wait you out. Instead, they will chase another CQ who is giving a more professional performance.

11-5. And now for the poor, overworked DE! We can't by any stretch of imagination determine where so many novices conceived the idea that the intermediate signal DE, transmitted between your call and that of the station you are calling, must be repeated *three* times. It isn't repeated at all; it is used only once between each series of calls. DE is simply a French expression meaning "from." Novices by the hundreds will make a call this way: "CQ CQ CQ DE DE DE KN4XXX KN4XXX KN4XXX." Interpreted it means "CQ CQ CQ FROM FROM FROM KN4XXX . . . ." Silly, isn't it? Do it right: "CQ CQ CQ DE KN4XXX KN4XXX KN4XXX."

11-6. Almost as much abused is a variation of this: "CQ CQ CQ DE KN4XX DE KN4XXX DE KN4XXX . . . ." Any listening station will stick with your CQ long enough to find out that KN4XXX is calling CQ. You will find the "three-by-three" method of calling CQ to be the most generally accepted.

11-7. The author has used a diminishing system of calling CQ with exceptionally good results. For example: "CQ CQ CQ DE W7OE W7OE W7OE CQ CQ DE W7OE W7OE CQ DE W7OE." This first group—CQ three times, DE once, then the call letters three times. The next group—CQ twice, DE once, followed by the call letters twice. Then we wind up the series by sending CQ once, DE once, and our call just once. As an on-the-air operator, be a good one. Pay particular attention to proper character formation with your key. Don't attempt to send faster than you receive: some more adept novice may "put you under the table." Besides, your character formation may suffer if you try to "pound brass" faster than your muscular co-ordination permits.

11-8. By now you've no doubt provided yourself with all of the essentials of the apprentice ham. These will include a log book or log sheets, one or more handbooks or construction manuals, an accurate timepiece, plenty of sharp pencils and pads of scratch paper, and a stock of QSL cards (either handmade or printed). You will have subscribed to, or at least buy at newsstands, the currently popular ham periodicals, so that you can keep abreast of ham activity and development. Of course, you will also have become a member of one or both of the two currently existing international organizations, "of, by, and for" the ham. These are the American Radio Relay League, Inc. and the QRP International Amateur Radio Club. Which you choose is, of course, your choice but we suggest that you send for literature from both to help you decide. The ARRL address is 225 Main Stree, Newington, Conn. 06111. For information on the QRP club, address the General Secretary-Treasurer, Jim Loring, Jr., WA1BEB, RFD "2" Gilead, Bethel, Maine 04217.

11-9. If you are in an area which supports a local amateur club, most certainly join it and attend meetings regularly. You'll find a grand bunch of guys and gals of all ages, with a wide variety of interest and experience in the various phases of ham radio. Club sessions are mostly informal—much "rag chewing" goes on, coffee and doughnut breaks are common, and ham jabber fills the air, much of which will rub off on you. Initially, it may seem to be gibberish, but it will rapidly form a pattern. Soon you will be an enthusiastic participant in field days; emergency operation; local, area, and national conventions—plus all the other good things ham radio has to offer.

11-10. More power to you, good hamming—and many, many pleasurable and exciting contacts. "73."

APPENDIX A

GLOSSARY OF STANDARD RADIO AND ELECTRICAL TERMS

Alternating Current (AC)—Electrical current flow which alternates in polarity at a definite, predetermined frequency.

Alternator—A generator used for producing AC voltages.

Ammeter—An instrument used to measure electrical current.

Ampere—The electrical unit of current flow.

Amplitude Modulation (AM)—A system whereby the amplitude of the radio frequency carrier is varied, corresponding to the intelligence signal.

Anode—*see* Plate.

Antenna (ANT)—The radiating portion of a radio transmitting station, or the collector wire of a radio receiver.

Audio Frequency (AF)—Any frequency within the range of human hearing (20 and 20,000 cps are considered the limits).

Buffer—An intermediate stage in a radio transmitter, between the oscillator and the final amplifier. May be one or more such buffer stages; usually serve to slightly amplify the output of the preceding stage and, through proper circuit components and adjustment, become frequency multipliers.

Bug—A semiautomatic telegraph key in which movement of a lever to one side produces a dot or a series of dots of equal duration and spacing, and movement to the other side produces a single dash.

Capacitor (Condenser)—Alternate elements of conducting and insulating material. The latter may be a solid dielectric, such as paper or mica, or simply air, as in variable capacitors.

Cathode—The electron-emitting element of a vacuum tube.

Choke—In power supplies and audio systems, a single coil of many turns of relatively fine wire wound around one leg of a soft-iron core.

Continuous Waves (CW)—Telegraphy.

Coulomb—The electrical unit of quantity.

Direct Current (DC)—An electric current (not necessarily constant in value) that flows in one direction only.

Dynamotor—A rotating device acting as both motor and generator.

Eastern Standard Time (EST)—The time zone corresponding to the mean local time of the 75th meridian west from Greenwich. (*Also see* Greenwich Mean Time.)

Electromotive Force (emf)—The force, or pressure, that produces the flow of electrical current.

Farad—The electrical unit of capacity.

Federal Communications Commission (FCC)—A commission set up by the United States government, with the power to regulate all U. S. communication systems.

Filament—The incandescent element in a vacuum electron tube or light bulb. In many vacuum tubes, the filament has no direct connection to any other element in the radio circuits, but serves to heat a cathode, in which case the filament is referred to as a heater.

Final Amplifier—The final tube in a radio transmitter. It introduces radio-frequency energy directly into the antenna circuits.

"Fist"—Slang for formation of code characters.

Frequency Modulation (FM)—A system whereby the frequency of the carrier is varied, corresponding to the intelligence signal.

Frequency Multiplier—Similar to a buffer stage, except the circuit components are calculated to permit tuning to a multiple of the frequency of the preceding stage. For example, proper design and adjustment will permit the output signal to be twice, three times, four times, etc., the frequency of the preceding stage. In such usage, the abbreviation applicable to the multiple is used; i.e., DBLR, for doubler (twice the frequency), TPLR for tripler (three times the frequency), QUAD for quadrupler, (four times the frequency), and so on.

Full-Wave Rectifier—A circuit in which both halves of the input AC waveform appear in the pulsating DC output.

Greenwich Mean Time (GMT)—A time reference based on the time when the sun crosses the meridian that passes through Greenwich, England (the mean solar time of Greenwich).

Grid—An electrode, mounted between the cathode and the anode of a vacuum tube, used to control the current flow.

Half-Wave Rectifier—A circuit in which only half of the input AC waveform appears in the pulsating DC output.

Harmonic Frequency—An integral multiple of any fundamental frequency.

Inductor—Wire or metallic tubing wound in a spiral around an iron core; or a circular core of insulating material; or, as with tubing or heavy wire, simply supported in air.

Intelligence Signal—The electrical signal corresponding to the information or intelligence being handled: sound, picture, code, etc.

Kilocycle (kc)—1000 cycles (per second). A unit of measurement for low, medium, and medium-high radio frequencies.

Megacycles (mc)—1000 *kilo*cycles, or 1,000,000 cycles (per second). A unit of measurement for high and ultrahigh radio frequencies.

Milliamperes (ma)—1/1000th of one ampere. In general use for measuring the various currents in radio transmitters.

Mobile Radio—A radio (transmitter and/or receiver) designed to operate while in motion.

Ohm—The electrical unit of resistance.

Ohmmeter—An instrument used to measure resistance.

Oscillator (OSC)—The circuit components which, when properly connected and adjusted, are capable of generating radio-frequency oscillations.

Parasitic Oscillation—Undesired self-sustaining random oscillations, different from the desired signal.

Plate—Also called the anode. An element within a vacuum-tube envelope which, by application of relatively high-voltage DC, attracts the electron flow from a heated filament or cathode.

Pulsating DC—A current that changes in value, but not in direction.

Quartz Crystal (XTAL)—A thin plate of rectangular quartz with the property of vibrating vigorously at only one frequency, dependent upon its thickness, when an external electrical potential is applied. Conversely, such mechanical vibration causes the crystal to also *generate* such currents. The quartz crystal is used as a frequency-controlling medium in radio transmitters.

Radio Frequency (RF)—Any frequency at which useful electromagnetic radiation can be obtained for communication purposes.

Resistor—A component that resists the flow of electrical current.

Resonance—A condition whereby the inductive reactance of a circuit equals and hence cancels the capacitive reactance.

Screen Grid—Similar in construction to the grid described earlier (*see* Grid). However, it is connected and operated somewhat differently in the radio-frequency circuits. The screen grid counteracts, to a large degree, the internal capacitance of a tube and, in the case of transmitters, generally eliminates the need for external neutralization of this effect.

Siphon Recorder—A device which reproduces high-speed automatic code transmissions onto a paper tape.

Skin Effect—The tendency of high-frequency currents to flow near the surface of a conductor, rather than through the entire cross-sectional area.

Splatter—Spurious frequencies, usually caused by overmodulation.

Variable-Frequency Oscillator (VFO)—An oscillator the frequency of which can be varied by a tuning control, as opposed to the fixed-frequency, crystal-controlled oscillator.

Volt—The electrical unit of pressure.

Voltmeter—An instrument used to measure electrical pressure (voltage, or emf).

Watt—A unit of electrical power.

Watt-Hour Meter—A meter used to measure and register electrical energy.

Wattmeter—An instrument used to measure electrical power.

APPENDIX B

FCC DISTRICT OFFICES

District	Address
1	Customhouse, Boston, Mass. 02109
2	Federal Bldg., 641 Washington St., New York, N. Y. 10014
3	New U. S. Customhouse, Philadelphia, Pa. 19106
4	U. S. Customhouse, Gay and Water Sts., Baltimore, Md. 21202
5	Federal Bldg., Norfolk, Va. 23510
6	2010 Atlanta Merchandise Mart, 240 Peachtree St., NE, Atlanta, Ga. 30303
7	P. O. Box 150, Federal Bldg., Miami, Fla. 33101
8	Federal Bldg., 600 South St., New Orleans, La. 70130
9	New Federal Office Bldg. (Room 5636), 515 Rusk Ave., Houston, Tex. 77002
10	States General Life Ins. Bldg., 708 Jackson St., Dallas, Tex. 75202
11	849 South Broadway, Los Angeles, Calif. 90014
12	Customhouse (555 Battery St.), San Francisco, Calif. 94126
13	New U. S. Courthouse, 620 SW Main St., Portland, Oreg. 97205
14	Federal Office Bldg. (First Ave. and Marion), Seattle, Wash. 98104
15	New Customhouse (19th between California and Stout Sts.), Denver, Colo. 80202
16	Federal Courts Bldg., 6th and Market Sts., St. Paul, Minn. 55102
17	Federal Office Bldg., 911 Walnut St., Kansas City, Mo. 64106
18	U. S. Courthouse, 219 South Clark St., Chicago, Ill. 60604
19	New Federal Bldg., Detroit, Mich. 48226
20	Post Office Bldg., Buffalo, N. Y. 14203
21	P. O. Box 1021, Federal Bldg., Honolulu, Hawaii, 96808
22	P. O. Box 2987, Federal Bldg., San Juan, P. R. 00903
23	P. O. Box 644, U. S. P. O. and Courthouse Bldg., Anchorage, Alaska 99501
24	1101 Pennsylvania Ave., NW., Room 10110, Washington, D. C. 20555
—	334 York St., Gettysburg, Pennsylvania 17325

APPENDIX C

RADIO AMATEUR NOVICE BANDS
AND TYPES OF EMISSION

Almost without exception, one of the examination questions will require you to be familiar with the frequency bands allotted for novice operation. Since this is purely a memory answer, we are listing these bands in Table I. Note that all bands are listed in *kilocycles*, except the 145-147 band, which appears in *megacycles* (don't let this confuse you).

Table 1. Novice Frequency Allocations

Frequency	*Emission*
3700–3750 kilocycles	CW only
7150–7200 kilocycles	CW only
21,100–21,250 kilocycles	CW only
145–147 megacycles	CW and MCW*

* Tone modulated continuous-wave telegraphy.

Up to now we have used the more common amateur designations of CW (telegraphy) and radiotelephone. You will also need to know a few of the formal FCC designations for the various types of emission. These designations are shown in Table II. For your novice examination, you need know only those marked with an asterisk (*).

Table II. Classification of Emission

Modulation or emission	Type of transmission	Sym.
1. Amplitude	Absence of any modulation	A0
	Telegraphy without the use of modulating audio frequency (on-off keying).	A1*
	Telegraphy by the keying of a modulating audio frequency or audio frequencies or by the keying of the modulated emission (special case: an unkeyed modulated emission).	A2*
	Telephony	A3*
	Facsimile	A4
	Television	A5
2. Frequency (or phase) modulated	Absence of any modulation	F0
	Telegraphy without the use of modulating audio frequency (frequency shift keying).	F1
	Telegraphy by the keying of a modulating audio frequency or audio frequencies or by the keying of the modulated emission (special case: an unkeyed emission modulated by audio frequency).	
	Telephony	F3
	Facsimile	F4
	Television	F5
3. Pulsed emissions	....	P